Contract Issues for Emergency Physicians
2nd Edition

Joseph P. Wood, MD, JD, FACEP, FAAEM, Editor

 Emergency Medicine Residents' Association

Editors

Joseph P. Wood, MD, JD, FACEP, FAAEM
Mayo Clinic Arizona
Editor in Chief

John J. Shufeldt, Jr. MD, JD, MBA, FACEP
The Shufeldt Law Firm
Paradise Valley, AZ
Co-editor

Michael T. Rapp, MD, JD, FACEP
Clinical Professor of Emergency Medicine
George Washington School of Medicine and Health Sciences
Co-editor

Authors

Sherri M. Arrigo, Esquire, Chicago, IL

Kimberly L. Horn, Chicago, IL

David Meyer, Esquire, Wheaton, IL

Marianne D. Meyer, Ann Arbor, MI

Gary Strange, MD, FACEP, Chicago, IL

Todd Taylor, MD, FACEP, Tempe, AZ

Steven Harris, Esquire, Chicago, IL

TABLE OF CONTENTS

ACKNOWLEDGEMENTS

EMRA would like to thank Joseph P. Wood, MD, JD, FACEP, FAAEM for his tremendous stewardship in developing and updating this publication for EMRA members. Always open to new suggestions and guided by his extensive experience and wisdom on contract issues and emergency medicine, EMRA could not have hoped for a more ideal person for this project.

EMRA would also like to thank Michael T. Rapp, MD, JD, FACEP and John J. Shufeldt, Jr. MD, JD, MBA, FACEP for reviewing the original draft and subsequent revisions of this book. With their own diverse experiences as emergency physicians, attorneys, and leaders within our specialty, they were both invaluable resources to the revision process.

Emergency Medicine Residents' Association Production Staff

Michele Byers, CAE – EMRA Executive Director

Barbara Voll – EMRA Assistant

Design Works Studio, Inc. – Cover design and layout

© Copyright 2000, 2007 Emergency Medicine Residents' Association
1125 Executive Circle, Irving, TX 75038-2522
972-550-0920, www.emra.org

The Emergency Medicine Residents' Association (EMRA) makes every effort to ensure that contributors to EMRA-sponsored publications are knowledgeable authorities in their field. Readers are, nevertheless, advised that the statements and opinions expressed in this book are provided as guidelines and should not be construed as EMRA policy unless specifically referred to as such. EMRA disclaims any liability or responsibility for the consequences of any actions taken in reliance on those statements or opinions. The materials contained herein are not intended to establish policy, procedure or a standard of care.

Additional copies of this publication are available from EMRA, Customer Service, 1-800-798-1822 extension 6 or 972-550-0920. Bulk purchase terms may be available.

An order form for this and other EMRA publications is available at www.emra.org.

Printed in the USA   ISBN: 1-929-854-12-9

INTRODUCTION

The basic principles of contract law rarely change. However, since the publication of the first edition of this monograph, several aspects of the business of emergency medicine have seen some interesting, distressing, and important developments. For example, some emergency physicians have faced the possibility of defending themselves in a lawsuit, without liability coverage, when the self-insured group they worked for entered into bankruptcy. Additionally, the federal government has essentially reversed itself by now allowing independent contractor physicians to assign billing rights to a group. However, the government remains vigilant in holding the individual responsible for billing and coding appropriately. Finally, many emergency physicians have challenged noncompete clauses and terminations without cause. These developments have prompted this revised and updated manual. Some chapters, such as "Billing Issues" (Chapter 8), and "Medical Malpractice Insurance" (Chapter 5), have been completely rewritten. Given the diversity of topics covered, new authors were recruited for some chapters and two new co-editors were added.

Years ago, it was not uncommon for emergency physicians to work at a hospital or for a group without a written employment contract. However, such arrangements would be highly unusual (and risky) in today's environment. This publication is intended to alert the emergency physician to issues central to entering into an employment or independent contractor agreement to provide medical services on behalf of a hospital or group. Reading this document cover to cover will not eliminate the need for you to obtain competent legal counsel before signing a contract, but this text will provide you with information and insights that will assist you in negotiating a contract and allow you to get the maximum benefit from the time spent with your attorney.

A well-written contract can get your employment relationship off to a good start. The contract should give you a clear understanding of what services your employer expects you to provide. It also should clearly state your compensation, including potential bonuses and benefits package. This clarity avoids misunderstandings that can sour the relationship between you and your employer. Because risk is inherent in any business venture, it is impossible for a contract to eliminate this element. However, a good contract will fairly allocate risk between the parties.

A fundamental question is whether you will be providing your services as an employee or independent contractor. In general, there are fewer administrative hassles in being an employee. Usually, your employer will provide a benefits package. In addition, the employer will make timely payments to the IRS on your behalf. For a variety of reasons, the IRS favors employee status. Alternatively, you may be asked to provide services as an independent contractor. Such an arrangement would give you greater latitude in designing your own benefits package. Also, you may be able to take some work-related deductions you would otherwise be denied in an employment situation. The pros and cons of these arrangements are discussed in further detail in Chapter 6.

Two controversial areas addressed in your contract are termination and "noncompetition" clauses. These clauses have provided significant controversy within the "house" of emergency medicine. Some emergency physicians have pointed out that many of the contracts offered contain unreasonable clauses that substantially undermine their job security. Such a situation may squelch a physician's ability to advocate on behalf of the patient. However, it is important to realize the legitimate business interest a group or hospital may be attempting to protect by the use of these contract clauses. Awareness of the issue and the needs of both sides will allow you to effectively negotiate a balanced approach.

Your employment or independent contractor agreement will undoubtedly address the issue of malpractice insurance. There is no room for ambiguities in this part of your contract. The contract should clearly state which party pays for the malpractice insurance, including "tail" coverage if a "claims-made" policy is used. Chapter 5 discusses the difference between "occurrence" policies and "claims-made" policies.

Finally, although most of the chapters of this book are written by attorneys, I hope you will pick up on the general theme that the relationship you establish is more important than the contract. The contract can be a tool that will bring clarity to your relationship, but the contract should always be viewed as a "tool." It is a means to an end and not the goal.

Contract Basics

In the Beginning

Virtually all contracts begin with a preamble. These sections are usually laden with legal jargon containing words such as "recitals" or "witnesseth." This preamble describes the parties to the contract and purposes of the contract. The important element here is to be aware of the "party" with whom you are contracting. Many physician contract holders incorporate as a means of facilitating accounting as well as limiting liability. The corporation is usually the entity used to enter into the employment contract. By signing a contract with a corporate entity, you are conceding you will rely solely on the corporation to fulfill the obligations owed to you in the contract. Generally, this is not a problem. However, there have been physicians who have not been paid for services rendered or had to pay their own malpractice premiums when the corporate entity, with which they had contracted, went into bankruptcy.

Contracting with a "thinly" capitalized corporation can be tricky. It is doubtful you would be successful in a request to have the major stockholder personally guarantee the obligations of the corporation. After all, people form corporations specifically to avoid personal liability. However, by working with your attorney, you can minimize your exposure. For instance, it may be safer for you to receive a higher compensation than initially offered and to use the increase in funds to pay your own malpractice premiums. You may also arrange to be paid biweekly or even weekly. Both of these techniques will avoid situations in which the corporation accrues a significant financial obligation toward you. Alternatively, you may ask the corporation to grant you a security interest in its accounts receivable. This will at least put you in line in front of other creditors should the corporation go bankrupt. Again, your personal attorney can be of great assistance to you in minimizing your risk in this regard.

OBLIGATIONS

Even as a non-attorney, you should be able to read through your contract and clearly understand the duties and services expected of you. Such obligations may be found in the body of the contract or in an addendum entitled "job description." If the job description is referenced in the contract, it in essence becomes an enforceable part of the agreement. In addition, the contract may incorporate by reference the medical staff bylaws, the hospital bylaws, and the department rules and regulations. After reviewing the contract and reference documents, you should be able to answer the following:

1. What are the minimum and maximum number of hours you are to be available per month for clinical shifts in the emergency department?
2. What administrative duties are you obligated to perform?
3. Are there "on-call" obligations?
4. Are you required to be board certified? If so, is a specific board required or understood?
5. Are there teaching obligations?
6. Are you obligated to cover clinical emergencies outside of the emergency department? If so, is the emergency department coverage such that you can realistically agree to this obligation?
7. Be aware of standard obligations, such as medical staff membership, state license, state-controlled substance number, DEA number, and Medicare/Medicaid participation. It takes several months to obtain a medical license in many states. In fact, it takes several months to obtain membership on the medical staff of many hospitals. Be sure you start the process early and the contract affords you adequate time to meet these obligations.

COMPENSATION

In general, you will assign your right to collect professional fees from patients and payers to the hospital or the group. In return, the group will compensate you with a fixed or hourly salary. These arrangements have some inherent complexities regarding the assignment of benefits for Medicare and Medicaid patients. This is discussed more fully in Chapter 8.

After reading your contract, the following should be clear:

1. Your compensation for clinical and administrative duties.
2. Bonuses (including benchmarks that must be met to trigger payment).
3. Benefits to be provided on your behalf; these include life insurance, health insurance, disability insurance, dental insurance, and paid time off. It should be clear whether the benefits are fixed in the contract or are subject to change.
4. Retirement contributions, profit-sharing contributions, and matched savings contributions may be provided as part of your compensation.
5. Reimbursement for expenses such as continuing medical education, licensure, professional society dues, and moving expenses should be outlined in the contract.

MEDICAL MALPRACTICE INSURANCE

The contract should clearly state which party is paying for the professional liability insurance. If the employer or group is purchasing insurance on your behalf, the contract should state that you will be named as an insured party. The insurance company should be obligated to provide you with proof of coverage. It should also be obligated to notify you of any changes in coverage or delinquent premiums. The contract should clearly state whether the insurance provided is of an "occurrence" or "claims-made" type. If a "claims-made" policy is used, the contract should clearly state which party is obligated to purchase the required "tail" coverage when necessary. Chapter 5 discusses malpractice insurance in depth. However, after reading your contract, you should be able to answer the following questions:

1. Which party is responsible for purchasing the malpractice insurance? Which party pays premiums?
2. What type of insurance is required ("occurrence" or "claims-made")?
3. What are the policy limits?
4. Which party is responsible for purchasing necessary "tail" insurance if a "claims-made" policy is used?
5. Does the contract specify the quality of the insurance carrier to be used? (Is it rated "A-" or better by a rating company such as A.M. Best Company?)
6. Does the contract require the policy to name the physician as an insured and provide a certificate of coverage?

TERMINATION

Most contracts are written for a fixed term, such as 1 or 2 years, with automatic renewal. However, the contracts usually provide for termination before the natural expiration by either party. The physician should retain the right to terminate the contract, without cause, on giving reasonable notice. Retaining this contract right rarely creates any controversy.

On the other hand, contract provisions that permit dismissal of the physician by the hospital or group, without cause, are the source of significant anxiety for many physicians. On the surface, it seems inconsistent for the physician to insist that he or she retain the right to terminate without cause but that the employer should not enjoy the same option. However, on closer scrutiny, there should be little doubt that the impact on the physician of a premature contract termination is likely to be great. The physician will experience a considerable loss of income and incur significant cost in replacing the job. Moreover, there may be some loss of reputation attached to being "fired." Conversely, a physician who terminates an employment contract because of a superior job offer elsewhere or a change in family circumstance is unlikely to have a significant economic impact on a hospital or group.

In reality, in most employment contracts and independent contractor agreements, the hospital or group will insist on retaining the right to terminate "without cause." Hospitals and groups believe there is a subjective element to many employment decisions, and consequently, they do not want to limit themselves to "for cause" terminations. However, you should be able to negotiate a reasonable notice requirement and possibly a severance package if this clause is invoked.

Most contracts also provide for termination "for cause." These clauses permit prompt termination of the contract for specific egregious behavior. You should accept these provisions as long as they fairly and specifically identify the behavior that triggers the termination.

Termination of contract carries with it inherent side issues such as termination of medical staff privileges and waiver of "due process." These issues, as well as noncompetition clauses, are discussed in detail in Chapter 9.

INDEMNIFICATION

Broad indemnification clauses are often included in independent contractor agreements. Such clauses are less frequently included in employment contracts. An indemnification clause obligates you to reimburse the hospital or group for financial liabilities they incur as a consequence of your conduct. For instance, under such a clause, you may be obligated to reimburse a hospital or group for malpractice awards in excess of insurance limits, for civil monetary awards, for government-imposed fines (EMTALA), or for IRS penalties associated with recharacterizing your status from independent contractor to employee. Usually, your professional liability policy will not cover these large expenditures. If the hospital or contract management groups insist on an indemnification clause, you should try to limit the scope to specifically enumerated situations. You should also insist on a mutual indemnification clause (i.e., the hospital or group will indemnify you against loss incurred by their breach of contract). This is an area of the contract that is rarely invoked, yet the stakes are potentially high. Agreeing to an indemnification clause is like agreeing to act as an insurer of the group or hospital for certain losses. You need to understand the chance of such an occurrence and the potential monetary risk before agreeing to accept this obligation.

MISCELLANEOUS

At the end of the contract, you will notice several miscellaneous sections common to most agreements. One section may be entitled "complete agreement." This section of the contract, in essence, states that the written document is the complete agreement between the parties. If the written document is the complete agreement, any oral promises made before or after the signing of the document would be unenforceable. You may use this clause to your advantage in politely insisting that promised benefits, bonuses, or schedule considerations are memorialized in the contract. Another section of the contract may be entitled "waiver." This section essentially states that ignoring a breach of the contract at one time does not preclude enforcement of a subsequent breach. The contract likely will discuss the right to assign the benefits and obligations of the document. Generally, the physician will not be given the right to assign the contract to another physician. On the other hand, the hospital or group will probably retain the right to assign the contract to a successor.

The following chapters will provide a more in-depth discussion of some of the substantive legal issues, including termination, noncompetition clauses, waiver of due process, assignment of billing, and medical malpractice. In addition, there are short chapters on negotiation strategy and the use of a search firm. Once again, this book is intended to be a primer that will assist you in understanding your contract and maximizing your time spent with your personal attorney.

2

SEARCH FIRMS:
THE PROS AND CONS

Editor's Note: Most residents are approached by a search firm at some time. This chapter is written by a recruiter who worked for a search firm in the past and currently works for an emergency medicine group. It explains the services provided and the mechanism of payment. Whether a resident should use a search firm is a personal choice.

From my experience, most of the best jobs are highly sought after. The hiring hospital or group is unlikely to use a search firm because they do not want to pay a fee to fill a position they would have easily filled anyway. Consequently, if you allow a search firm to "shop" you around, you should make it clear that you retain the right to do your own job search and that no fee will be owed (by either you or the practice) if you initiated the contact.

On the other hand, many physicians are helped enormously by a good search executive. A good search professional can help educate the physician on local market conditions pertaining to salaries and benefits. The search professional can also provide insights on the practice. An excellent search executive will also help you market yourself by helping prepare your curriculum vitae and giving you feedback after your interviews.

Many residents ask why they use search firms and why hospitals/groups use a search firm. Recruitment companies have traditionally been engaged by hospitals or physician groups to identify candidates to fill an emergency department vacancy. However, in the past several years the role of search firms has changed. Some search firms do both permanent placement and locum tenens. This way, they provide short-term and long-term solutions for hospitals and groups. A physician may engage a firm to seek out alternative job opportunities and thereby request that a recruitment firm confidentially identify potential hospitals or groups that may have an opening and/or interest. In the case of the physician who is seeking alternative job opportunities, the physician's name is not disclosed. They may also use a search firm if they want to travel or have the flexibility of a locums position.

Depending on the type of position (chairperson, director, staff, and so on), a university, hospital, or group may elect to use a search firm to perform a regional or national search to fill a permanent position. The decision to use a search firm is often based on need and institutional preferences and policies. Factors that influence decisions include available internal resources, the costs versus benefits at a search firm, the degree of need, the time of the year, the position recruited, the effectiveness of alternative methods (i.e., advertisements, local networking), and search committee preferences. Ultimately, it is the value relative to the need that influences a hospital or group to use an external recruitment firm. There are different levels of service provided by a search firm, and this determines the search fee.

SEARCH FEE

In today's market, most search services are engaged by the hospital, group, or other entity that will be hiring the physician. Most search firms operate and contract in one of two methods. The methodologies range from a retained search agreement to a contingency level of service. Under the retained method, the search firm is paid a percentage of the service fee to initiate the search. This retainer fee typically ranges from $3,000 to $5,000 in most cases and is a percentage of the total search fee. Retainers are paid on a monthly basis or as a function of search services performed over a period of time. The remaining balance of the search service fee is paid to the search firm on completion of the recruitment assignment with a successful candidate. Depending on the recruitment company and the services to be rendered, the total search fee ranges from $12,000 to $25,000.

A search firm can be engaged on an exclusive basis (i.e., the firm is the only agent for the search), and all candidates are serviced by the firm or the search can be open to one or more firms on a contingency basis. Under a retained, exclusive search, all physician candidates under consideration will be contacted and screened by the recruitment firm. Under this scenario, the physician does not make the decision to use a search firm but rather receives the inherent recruitment services as engaged by the hospital or group. There is no cost to the physician. Furthermore, no fee should be deducted from your compensation offer.

It is also important to understand that the search fee paid is for services rendered for all candidates contacted during the entire process. Under no circumstances should the successful candidate pay directly or indirectly for the recruitment services engaged by the hospital or group. Depending on the services rendered and the duration of the search, the number of physician candidate contacts may range from 500 to 2,500+. Based on a search fee of $20,000, the prorated cost for each candidate ranges from $8.00 to $40.00. Very simply, if you are the successful candidate, you are not responsible for the search service fee, let alone the fee associated with all of the other candidates.

The contingency method of recruitment involves no retainer fee. Under these services, the total fee is paid to the recruitment company when the successful candidate is recruited. Once again, depending on the recruitment company and services rendered, the recruitment fee ranges from $10,000 to $23,000. Under a contingency recruitment agreement, there are very few, if any, performance guarantees provided by the search firm. Under the contingency search scenario, the recruitment firm carries the entire cost of search until the search is completed. It is a full-risk expense contract for the search firm in the event a successful candidate is not recruited. In most cases, a contingency search is conducted by more than one firm.

If a physician contacts a search firm for a confidential job search or if a search firm contacts a physician, it is totally a matter of physician preference whether to use the services of the recruitment company. In today's short supply market of well-trained emergency physicians, and in many other cases, the recruitment fee is paid by the hospital or group that contracts with the recruitment firm for services. As the supply/demand ratio changes in the future, the need for recruitment services or the responsibility for paying fees may change.

If a physician uses a search firm for locums work, the firm will pay the physician an hourly rate, pay for travel expenses, and pay the physician's malpractice insurance. These costs (most of which the hospital or group would have anyway if they employed the physician directly) are passed along to the hospital or group contracting with the firm along with a fee.

THE PROS

As with most service companies, search firms vary greatly in terms of resources, experience, knowledge base, professionalism, and level of services. There are numerous advantages and disadvantages to the use of a search firm. A reputable search firm should always add value to your job search and maintain confidentiality. A reputable search firm should offer the following services and advantages:

1. Assist in your career planning by asking specific questions to help you with the personal and professional parameters of your search; some firms offer a career planning outline/checklist to help with these decisions.
2. Provide information relative to the job details and knowledge relative to such issues as compensation, contract terminology, malpractice issues, and benefits offered.
3. Maintain a job search database and advise you of jobs meeting your personal and professional parameters; if requested, they will conduct a confidential networking effort to identify potential job openings.
4. As appropriate, identify key decision makers and establish contact with the potential employer regarding openings that are desirable, and present your curriculum vitae to facilitate initial contact and provide a value-added introduction.
5. Provide persistence to ensure that the initial contact and interview process proceed in a timely and organized manner.
6. Provide assistance to arrange the interview details, and provide insight regarding the internal process and players.
7. After the interview, provide candid and reliable interview feedback, and assist with providing reimbursement for your interview expenses.
8. Assist with contract negotiation to facilitate a "win-win" closure.

THE CONS

There are some potential disadvantages to working with a search firm. To make it a positive experience, talk to the person with whom you are working about how they can best help you. Some of the most common concerns/disadvantages of using a search firm are listed below:

1. Although search firms represent a wide variety of positions, they may not be working with hospitals or groups in the area you want.
2. Many emergency departments in the more popular areas, such as California and Texas, are run by large groups who do not use search firms.
3. Some hospitals or groups may choose a candidate who is not working with a search firm over one who is to avoid paying a search fee even though the hospital or group has contracted for recruitment services.
4. Physicians believe they will receive less compensation or not receive a signing bonus from the hospital or group if they find a position through a search firm. This may or may not be true depending on the ethics and principles of the hospital or group.

There are ways to turn these concerns/disadvantages into positive aspects that work to your advantage. A search firm cannot know about every position available, so if there is a specific area in which you are interested, ask the search firm to contact hospitals/groups in that area for you. Work with the search firm to develop a plan to target hospitals/groups that meet your parameters. If you want to move to an area that is predominantly controlled by groups, ask them for the names. This will at least get you started in contacting the right people.

Unfortunately, there are some hospitals/groups that will choose one physician over another physician simply to avoid paying a search fee. Remember that just as a hospital or group contracts a law firm for its legal services, they also contract a search firm for their recruitment services. Therefore, two physicians who apply for the same position should be treated equally regardless of whether they contacted the hospital/group on their own or through a search firm. The physician's qualifications, education, and personality and how well he or she would fit in should be the deciding factors, not whether he or she came through a search firm.

Search firms can bring a lot of value to a hospital, group, and physician. To ensure it is a positive and beneficial experience, choose a search firm that is professional and reputable and can meet your goals.

3

NEGOTIATING YOUR CONTRACT

Negotiation, like medicine, is an art that can be studied and practiced. Like medicine, it requires forethought, patience, cognitive skills, and intuitiveness. Emergency physicians possess all these skills. With this skills set comes a problem inherent to our profession—the ability to make rapid decisions. Emergency physicians develop the ability to make critical decisions with imperfect information, rapidly and conclusively. It is this trait or ability that can cause problems. Until recently, the love of rapid analysis and decision making caused me problems. This chapter will help you to avoid the same traps that I plunged into by being decisive and efficiency driven as opposed to being patient and information driven.

We have been negotiating since childhood—first with our parents and siblings, then with our friends and classmates, and finally with coworkers and patients. How many times have you said, "I know a spinal tap sounds painful; however, if you curl up in a tight ball and hold very still, it will be over in a few minutes and we can make sure you don't have meningitis." That was a negotiation. You are trading information gained from the lumbar puncture for the patient's consent to have a lumbar puncture performed. We have all witnessed the exchange between a physician who has limited negotiation skills and a resistant patient. The patient rarely does what the physician asks and usually leaves against medical advice or, at the very least, with the administrator's name and telephone number.

I have referenced a number of excellent texts about negotiation. I will borrow from them for this short essay because they represent the state-of-the-art regarding negotiation strategy and techniques. Negotiation is about information and leverage. The key to a successful outcome depends on your ability to acquire information, manage leverage, design an offer and concession strategy, and, finally, to control the agenda.

SETTING THE GROUND RULES

I have been down to the final clause of a contract only to have the person I was negotiating with say that he is not the decision maker and will have to run it by his superior. This is a very common tactic because it allows him to defer the decision and make someone else with whom you have no relationship the final determining factor. It is crucial at the outset to determine if the individual you are negotiating with has the final say and, if not, what are their limits of authority.

INFORMATION IS POWER

Suppose you are out buying a stereo and you are in Best Buy®. Compare the following possible approaches for their effectiveness: "I think you are charging too much for this stereo, I would not be willing to spend that amount, I can always go elsewhere." Compare that exchange to "I was at your competitor, Stereo Mart, on Mill Avenue and they have the same model listed for $150 dollars below your price including installation. If you can beat that deal, I will buy it from you today." In the second example, you have demonstrated that you have done your homework and are willing to take your business elsewhere if the salesperson is unwilling or unable to beat the price of their competitor.

The same holds true in contract negotiation. Before entering into contract negotiations, it is crucial for you to understand the organizational and legal structures of the prospective group. This will allow you to come to the table fully prepared to address the relevant issues. Often, simply asking other members of the group is the most effective step toward gaining the necessary understanding. For example, in negotiation with a large national group, the parameters that govern the amount of latitude available in the contract may be exceedingly narrow. It would be imprudent for large groups to allow for a great deal of variation in individual physicians' contracts. The task of managing a wide variety of special circumstances on a national scale would prove overwhelmingly daunting. In a small group, however, there often exists wide latitude in the ranges of salary and contract specifics.

Equally vital for the negotiating physician is a firm grasp of the dynamics of the market, with particular emphasis on salary and benefit ranges. The laws of supply and demand that so absolutely govern the commercial world apply to emergency medicine as well. To understand the application of these principals, one must observe relevant statistics including the length of time required for employers to fill similar positions. Techniques such as keeping track of the number of months (or issues) that specific job ads run in various publications can prove to be invaluable. Although a "soft" sign, this technique will serve as a gauge of the supply-and-demand curve for a particular area. If the emergency department is in a low-demand area, the job seeker may reasonably expect contract holders to offer creative incentives. Alternatively, physicians in areas of abundant supply must anticipate an atmosphere of greater competition. Knowledge of these market specifics is an integral part of negotiating a favorable contract.

NEGOTIATION OVERVIEW

INTRODUCTIONS AND FINDING COMMON GROUND

Contact negotiations actually begin the moment you walk into the room or pick up the telephone. Your physical appearance, your mannerisms, and what you are wearing speak volumes about your character and ability. It is useful to start out the discussion searching for common personal experiences or interests. It is much easier negotiating with someone with whom you have developed at least some sort of relationship or shared experience. Marty Latz, the author of *Gain the Edge*, calls this the "big schmooze."

INFORMATION GATHERING

Now that you know information is power, how do you get it? The best way is to gather as much as you can before the interview. Then, use the interview or negotiation to fill in the gaps. During the negotiation, ask questions. Start out with open-ended questions and move to closed-ended questions as you get closer to all the information you need. Use the power of silence to extract as much information as possible. Silence is uncomfortable for many people who will fill the silence with useful information, so be patient.

Another tip to gain information is to leave your ego at the door. Do not let your ego get in the way of your ability to communicate openly. This requires sincerity and the establishment of trust. Begging the question, how do you establish trust? You may start out by making a minor concession early in the course of the negotiation. For example, you may agree to move up your projected start time by a week. Also, stress the importance of your reputation as a trustworthy individual and your desire to have them independently confirm your trustworthiness. Last, communicate using clear unambiguous statements and commitments. You may even want to put early commitments in writing, thereby firmly establishing your intentions of being honorable.

SEPARATE THE ISSUES FROM THE PEOPLE

Negotiations are between individuals who bring to the table their own biases and idiosyncrasies. With these personality traits come negotiating styles that may be quite different or very similar to your own. To rise above personality- or ego-driven communication, lay out the issues that need to be resolved. You now share common goals—resolving the issues. For example, if the negotiation is between yourself and the managing member of the group, the simple fact that you are at this stage probably means that the group actually wants to make you an offer. So, lay out the issues: (1) start date, (2) salary, (3) CME allowance, (4) vacation and benefits, etc. It serves to narrow the scope of the discussion by having all the issues on the table.

MAXIMIZE LEVERAGE

You may be saying, "I have no leverage, there are a hundred people behind me who would all jump at the chance for this job, I better just be thankful for the opportunity." Who has more leverage—the managing partner who is conducting the interview or the fresh-faced emergency medicine residency graduate? The answer is, it depends! If the managing partner knows she has multiple shifts to cover, mostly nights and weekends, and is losing an employee on maternity leave, the answer is the recent graduate.

Before the negotiation, evaluate each side's leverage. Determine how badly they want you and why. This is where all the information you gathered comes in handy. Also, take a critical look at your own leverage. How badly do you need this job? What determines the BATNA[1] (the best alternative to a negotiated agreement)? This is your walk-away point. Before the negotiation, you need to seek alternatives to the particular job for which you are negotiating. You also need to evaluate the other side's BATNA. Who will they get, and what will it cost them if the deal with you does not work out? What is the competition in the marketplace? Who else is applying for the job?

HOW DO YOU ENHANCE LEVERAGE?

Leverage is dynamic. If the partner in the example above hired two residents that morning, your leverage became much less powerful. If, on the other hand, the partner found out that another partner is quitting to go to law school, your leverage just became much better. When would you rather strike? After the other two are hired or immediately after the other partner gives notice? Striking while the iron is hot is key to getting the best possible result. Leverage is enhanced by your knowledge of the marketplace and your "value" in the particular environment.

Tactically share information with the other side that enhances their perception of your leverage. You can tell them how many other job opportunities there are in the area, what sort of salaries those in your peer group are commanding, and what other perks are being offered with those contracts. Do not be deceitful. If you try to bluff them and are called on it, you have lost all credibility in the negotiation. Also, that reputation will stick with you—emergency medicine is a small community and reputations, like influenza, travel through communities very quickly.

EMPLOYEE FAIR OBJECTIVE CRITERIA

Everyone wants a "fair" deal. The question arises as to what constitutes "fairness" and whose definition is used to determine what is "fair." What do you do when the response to your request is met with, "We can't do that, this is the way we have always done it"?

Before the negotiation, determine your most reliable, independent standard. This may be salary reviews by location, salary precedents, and industry standards. How do you counter standards when the information is not advantageous to your cause? Discuss and document why you are different, how the industry standard is inapplicable to you, and why you command more. The same is true with precedent or tradition. Find out if they have made exceptions previously, to whom those exceptions applied, and when they made them. Discuss how your experience or talent is analogous to previous exceptions. Or, conversely, use a "circumstances have changed" argument. Argue that the facts that surrounded the previously held traditions have changed, making those traditions obsolete or inapplicable to today's market.

DESIGN AN OFFER-CONCESSION STRATEGY

Everyone wants a deal. They want to believe that they got the biggest bang for their buck. Denying your counterpart this belief will actually hurt you in the process. In this respect, the simple act of give and take is not only part of the process, it is crucial to the process. For example, if you are like many emergency physicians, you may use the technique of, "Let's quit beating around the bush and just get down to brass tacks." Instead of each party working toward some middle ground, you may suggest the middle ground and start there in an effort to save time, etc. If the average hourly salary in an area is $110, you may just suggest that figure in an effort to be reasonable and efficient. If the group's manager was going to start at $85 and move up to a $110, what do you think she now is going to aim for? She is going to believe that she can get you for $97.50, the midpoint between your first offer and her first anticipated offer. Why don't you start at $160 and work toward a middle of $125? Because unless you have fair, objective criteria that $160 is at least plausible, you will lose credibility at the outset. The $160 starting point will be viewed exactly as what it is: a "shoot for the moon" offer. Conversely, when your first offer is aggressive, yet based on independent standards, you can defend the offer with those independent verifications.

MAKING THE FIRST OFFER

Do you want to make the first offer? Some advantages to making the first offer are that it sets the stage and begins to define the expectations. It may also elicit a genuine reaction from your counterpart. However, when you make the first offer, you need to have market data. The other side will gain important information from your offer and may use it to bracket the final outcome. *Bracketing* is a method of moving as far in the opposite direction from the suspected endpoint of your offer. Last, by making the first offer, you may seem too eager and lose some important leverage.

Many people start the offer concession process too soon. They want to "get right down to it." There are significant disadvantages to doing this. First off, you may not have all the information you need to make intelligent choices. Thinking through the offer-concession strategy is a must inasmuch as it forces you to get into your partner's head, thereby allowing you to anticipate his counters. Prospectively determining your counterpart's response before your offer or concession will help you determine what should be the magnitude of your initial response.

CONTROL THE AGENDA

Controlling the agenda can make a difference in the negotiation. Deciding when, where, and which items to include in the negotiation will ultimately help determine the outcome. Take the initiative and write out the agenda before the meeting. Present the agenda and negotiate it using the same techniques suggested. You will be surprised; often, the one who takes the initiative to write out the agenda sets the tone and pace.

Determine and agree on deadlines. Are you waiting for other job offers? Is the group waiting for responses from other candidates? Collectively decide what time frames will apply. Is this an agreement that needs to be reached within a few days, or will a couple of weeks be acceptable? Set the time frames and stick to them. When people have deadlines with discernable consequences, they are more likely to stick to them.

More likely than not, you will be negotiating on their turf. This may be a disadvantage; however, you can learn valuable information by quietly observing the office décor and personal effects. Are there family pictures present? What sort of hobbies or interests does your counterpart have? Is there any common ground based on those hobbies or interests? Are the hobbies particularly risky? Are there pictures of them base-jumping, scuba diving, or heli-skiing hanging on the wall? If so, you are probably not talking to the most risk-adverse member of the group. Knowing that prospectively should help you gauge their responses.

CONCLUSIONS

Negotiating, like medicine, is a skill that can be learned and practiced.Many attributes of a successful emergency physician can actually be detrimental in negotiating. Our need to make rapid decisions with imperfect information will often times not leave us with the best deal. By using the techniques described, your negotiating style will improve, and you will be better prepared to get the best offer available!

REFERENCES

1. Fisher, Roger, Ury, William, and Patton Bruce (2002). *Getting to Yes: Negotiating Without Giving In*. New York, Penguin Books.

GENERAL REFERENCES

– Latz, Martin (2004). *Gain the Edge: Negotiating to Get What You Want*. New York, St. Martins Press.
– Ury, William (1991). *Getting Past No: Negotiating With Difficult People*. New York, Penguin Books.

4

EQUITY

Editor's Note: Many physicians who join a group practice are offered "partnership" after a trial period. In this chapter, the author discusses the concept of "equity" in a group practice. "Equity" is essentially a synonym for an "ownership" interest in the group. This can be in the form of a partnership or as a stock holder of a corporation. However, as the author explains, not everyone who holds equity in the group holds the same power to direct the affairs of the group or shares in the profits equally. Income distribution and governance of the group are controlled by the corporate or partnership bylaws or contractual agreements between the equity holders.

EQUITY

An important consideration in evaluating an emergency medicine position is the potential for acquiring an equity or ownership interest in the practice. Although the details of ownership interests vary considerably among groups, normally the principal value of equity includes greater employment security, a greater share of practice revenue, and a greater opportunity to participate in leadership and management decisions.

In some situations, there is also the potential that the ownership interest will increase in value over time and be a source of profit for a physician owner at redemption or sale. In fact, during the heyday of mergers and acquisitions of emergency medicine practices in the early 1990s, some emergency physicians profited handsomely through the sale of practices or even through establishing publicly traded companies based on holding emergency department contracts. This is much less common today, but for groups where growth in number of emergency department contracts is actively pursued, the chance of increasing the value of an equity interest remains.

Many practice opportunities, of course, will not offer any ownership interest. For example, physician employees of hospitals, academic medical centers, or government agencies typically do not acquire equity in a practice. Similarly, large contract groups do not offer equity, except insofar as publicly traded stock may be purchased for corporations holding hospital contracts. In some instances, one or more physicians who are not willing to share ownership equity with other physicians may hold the contract.

Although most physicians intuitively want an ownership interest, positions that do not offer equity are not necessarily inferior to those that do. The primary issues for most physicians are income, income growth, job security, and the opportunity to participate in leadership and management. These issues exist in any practice situation and, regardless of the practice structure, most often require some contractual agreement.

Acquiring equity in a practice always will have a cost and will always have a value. In weighing these elements, it is important to obtain as much detail as possible. Whether the equity interest will be worth the cost will ultimately depend on the individual physician's personal, financial, and career goals and must be evaluated individually in that context.

Whether or not equity is offered to physicians joining a practice, a significant issue can be the degree of disparity between the income of owners and non-owners. While all groups afford greater benefits to owners based on the greater degree of service and commitment, groups have widely varying philosophies on how great the financial disparity should be. Such information is often very closely held. Nevertheless, in evaluating any practice opportunity, it is important to follow the money trail and to try to determine the source of the practice revenues and what happens to those revenues. There may be special bonus structures, stipends, special vacation allocations, or other financial benefits that accrue only to owners with some preferences allocated only to those who have been owners longer. Inevitably, the philosophy of the group on ownership preferences will affect the route to obtaining an ownership interest and the cost of and value of the ownership interest.

FORMS OF BUSINESS OWNERSHIP

It is important to be familiar with the three basic forms of business ownership to fully understand the issue of obtaining an equity interest in an emergency medicine practice—sole proprietorship, partnership, and corporation.

Sole Proprietorship

In a sole proprietorship, a single individual owns the business. In that case, the individual holds all the rights and obligations pertaining to the business, including the assets, total management control of the business, the right to any profits, and the responsibility for all the liabilities. Formerly, it was common for a single physician to hold a hospital contract and employ or contract with the remainder of the group's physicians. Today, hospital contracts are usually held by groups of physicians, although sole proprietorships still do occur. If the contract is held by a sole proprietor or by a corporation wholly owned by an individual, there is no opportunity for equity, and all prerogatives of the physician would be defined by contract.

Partnership

Many physicians refer to acquiring equity in a group as "becoming a partner." However, few emergency physician groups are actually structured as partnerships. The classic general partnership gives each partner an equal share of the equity, management control, and share of the profits. A principal reason that most physicians today do not use the partnership model is because each general partner is also responsible for the liabilities of other partners. In a medical practice, this means that one partner is potentially financially responsible for the malpractice of another. Thus, a partner who had no involvement with a patient can still be held financially liable for the malpractice of a partner. Some emergency medicine groups are structured as limited partnerships. In this case, the liabilities of the partnership are limited and accrue only to the general partners while management control is vested with the general partners.

Corporation

By far the most common business structure for physician groups is the corporation. In a corporate structure, the ownership interest of a shareholder is defined by the percentage of the share of the corporation owned. Thus, each member of a physician group may be a shareholder but still have a much different interest than another physician.

Corporations are characterized by separation of management control from ownership. In a general partnership, each general partner shares in the management. However, in a corporation, the board of directors, not the shareholders, has management control. Thus, one can have an equity interest by virtue of being a shareholder but no say in management. To have a say in management, one must be on the board of directors. To control management, one would need to have a sufficient number of shares to be able to elect a majority of the board of directors.

This separation of management control and ownership is the reason that solely becoming a shareholder of the physician group's corporation does not provide any guarantees in terms of job security or income. These issues are decided by the board of directors. Therefore, even shareholders typically have such issues dealt with in an employment or other contract. In some instances, groups do not have such formalities in place, and financial and employment issues are decided on an ongoing basis by the board of directors. In such situations, the importance of board membership is apparent.

The third feature of a corporation is limited liability. Limited liability means that, unlike a general partnership, the financial risk to the shareholder of a corporation is limited to the cost of the shares purchased. Although shares may become worthless, creditors of the corporation cannot normally go to shareholders themselves to collect debts of a corporation.

Evaluating a Potential Ownership Opportunity

There may be some reluctance for a young physician to ask the necessary questions to fully understand the cost and benefits of selecting a group that has an ownership track. However, nearly every emergency medicine group is unique unto itself, and it is necessary to explore these details if one is to be able to evaluate the opportunity that may be offered by one group compared with another.

What Does It Cost?

Emergency medicine groups that do offer an ownership opportunity have varying buy-in requirements or ownership tracks. "Sweat equity" is part of becoming an owner in nearly every emergency medicine practice. Typically, this means some requirement for duration of employment that varies from as little as one year to as long as seven or more years. During those years, the physician forgoes a certain amount of income that is earned or that would otherwise be forthcoming. It is important to quantify the total amount of the lost income over the required practice time to fully understand the cost.

It is also important to have a clear understanding of the likelihood of an ownership opportunity being offered. Some groups routinely offer an ownership interest after a certain period of time. Others may ultimately offer an ownership interest to only a small portion of physicians who accept employment. The selection criteria and the process for selection must be mutually understood, and ideally these understandings will be incorporated into the employment agreement. Without this, one may invest several years in a group practice with reduced income and opportunity costs based on an unrealistic expectation for an equity interest.

In addition to "sweat equity," some groups require a cash buy-in. Where a cash buy-in is required, it is more likely that the group has actual hard assets, such as accounts receivable or real estate ownership of an office or a practice site. Where a cash buy-in is required, it is important to understand clearly what is being acquired for that money.

WHAT IS IT WORTH?

The best way to evaluate the potential value of an equity or ownership interest in an emergency medicine practice is the same way that a potential buyer of an entire business evaluates its worth. This process is called "due diligence." It involves gaining a full understanding of the business, its financial status, its historical income, its likelihood to continue to generate that amount of income, its prospects for growth, any actual or contingent liabilities, and any risks to the business. While seeking such information may seem inappropriate, it is the best safeguard against spending years preparing to acquire equity in a practice only to find out such equity is of little or no value. Additionally, the willingness or unwillingness of a group to share information on such aspects of the practice will be informative as to the general openness of the group management with its nonequity physicians.

WHAT WILL I GET BY BECOMING AN OWNER?

It is important to be clear as to what four features of business ownership the physician will acquire by becoming an owner: the actual equity or ownership interest, management control, a right to a share of the profits, and the right to continue as a member of the practice.

OWNERSHIP INTEREST

Typically, the tangible ownership interest obtained when acquiring equity in an emergency medicine group practice will be shares of a corporation. However, unlike owning publicly traded stock, the shares of a closely held corporation usually cannot be sold. Not only is there generally no market for such stock, but normally restrictions are placed on the award of stock prohibiting sale of the shares except to another shareholder, or the corporation itself, using a specified price methodology.

The actual value of the shares, therefore, will usually depend on agreements among the shareholders and the corporation for redemption of the shares. These include shareholder agreements on price to be paid on redemption of shares when leaving the group, agreements for payments to shareholders on redemption of shares at retirement, special bonus payments limited to shareholders, or other shareholder preferences.

The formula used to price the shares of stock for redemption varies greatly among groups. This makes it important to understand the basis for determining the redemption price. Often, this price may simply be the amount paid for the shares at buy-in. At other times, it may reflect book value of the corporation. Usually, there is no expectation of a significant rise in the value of the shares over time. However, again, this varies. The possibility for an increase in value is greatest where the practice pursues an active growth strategy, where the group acquires new contracts regularly, where there is a limited number of owners compared with nonowners, where there is a history of increasing cost of buy-in for subsequent owners, and where there is a history of increasing payment at redemption for departing owners.

MANAGEMENT CONTROL

As mentioned previously, the management control of a corporation is vested in the board of directors. To have a say in the management of the corporation, then, it is necessary to be a member of the board of directors or appointed or employed by the corporation in a management position. Some groups make the number of seats on the board of directors the same as the number of shareholders. This can become unwieldy after the group reaches a certain size, resulting in either a smaller number of board members or appointment of an executive committee on which only certain board members serve. Regardless, it is important to understand the management structure, the relative numbers of board seats compared with shareholders, how management decisions are made and who has input into them, and the likelihood that, if the group maintains a corporate structure, becoming a shareholder will also mean becoming a member of the board of directors.

SHARE OF THE PROFITS

Becoming a shareholder of a corporation classically gives no right to a share in the profits of the corporation. There are certain hybrid corporate business forms that have the feature of proportionately sharing profits, as do partnerships. Corporations designated as a Subchapter S corporations for IRS tax purposes are one example. Another example is the limited liability corporation (LLC), which at times is used for emergency medicine practices. Even absent this, many emergency medicine groups have a formal process or perhaps an agreement as to how the profits of the practice are distributed and to whom. It is important to understand this fully, because a primary benefit from ownership is the ability to share in the profits.

RIGHT TO A JOB

A major interest of any physician who invests the time and money necessary to obtain an equity interest in a practice is the ability to be secure as a member of the practice. However, ownership in a corporate structure, or even a partnership, gives no specific job security or rights against being terminated. Absent an agreement, the majority of the members of the board of directors could terminate any employee, including a shareholder employee. In some groups, this authority may be even delegated to the corporation president. Frequently, there are agreements among the shareholders to limit the ability of the group to terminate a shareholder, such as requiring a supramajority (e.g., requiring a two-thirds vote of the board of directors). In other situations, however, there is no specific agreement. Because of the significance of job security to an equity owner, it is important to understand what special provisions, if any, apply to physicians in the group that hold an equity interest.

WHAT IS THE VALUE OF THE PRACTICE?

Although the rights and obligations previously discussed are of major importance to the emergency physician, in considering an opportunity for an ownership interest, it is worthwhile to consider the value of the practice as a business. This will depend on many factors. However, insofar as job security and the potential financial rewards of ownership are important, this will be affected significantly by the basic strength and success of the emergency medicine practice.

HOSPITAL CONTRACT

The most valuable asset of any emergency medicine group normally consists of the contract(s) held with one or more hospitals. Without the emergency department contract, there is no ability of emergency physicians to practice at a given hospital in a way that they can retain the total benefit of the fees they generate. The value of an ownership interest in a practice is therefore critically dependent on the likelihood that hospital contract(s) will be retained or increased. Although it is fair to say that no emergency department contract is completely secure, in evaluating the value of a potential equity interest in a practice, it is nevertheless important to consider whether there are any apparent indications that increase the potential for instability of the emergency department contract.

There are certain circumstances that heighten the possibility of emergency department contract change. One set of factors relates to significant changes and transitions of the hospital itself. Examples include major growth of patient volume, making it difficult to meet patient care demands; senior leadership changes, especially a change of administrator whose attitude toward the group may not be as favorable; or hospital mergers or separations from previously merged hospital systems, which may be accompanied by governance or administrative changes.

Another set of factors that increase the potential for instability of an emergency department contract relates to the group itself. A rapidly growing group that is adding contracts may find conflict resulting from having contracted with competing hospitals. A change in the leadership of the emergency department physician group such as through retirement of the leader of the group can also be of significant impact, because the group leader may have the primary relationship with the hospital administration.

A third set of factors that may impact an emergency department contract relates to external influences. Examples of stakeholders who can influence the hospital leadership significantly are third party payers, local government administrators, or the EMS system. Any major dissatisfaction with the emergency department group by such parties can create an adverse environment for the emergency department group.

In addition to making inquiries about the factors discussed, it is worthwhile to have some understanding of the specifics of the contractual relationship with the hospital. Examples are the degree to which the group appears to be meeting the needs of the many customers a group must serve; the length of the contract, how often it needs to be renewed, and what stage of renewal the contract is in;

whether there are any known issues that would impact the potential for renewal; in whose name is the contract, the group, or an individual; who is the primary contact with the administration; and whether the group has a succession plan to deal with the possibility that the key figure with regard to retaining the contract may leave or retire.

REVENUE

A good indicator of the strength of the emergency medicine practice is the total revenue and the rate of growth of revenue. A prospective physician may not be told the total revenue but likely would be told the rate of growth or at least the rate of growth of the patient census in the hospital. A falling revenue stream or falling patient census base can be a source of concern about the prospects for the practice.

ACCOUNTS RECEIVABLE

Physician groups have different contractual arrangements with hospitals with respect to accounts receivable. Some physician groups have arrangements with hospitals, whereby they assign the physician fees to the hospital, which in turn remits an estimated amount to the group the month after services are performed. In such cases, the group owns no accounts receivable.

However, most physician groups no longer have such arrangements but instead maintain accounts that have been billed but not yet collected. What this means is that if a practice ceases operations, fees will be collected over an extended time period afterward. At times, physician groups require equity owners to buy-in to the accounts receivable. At other times, the "sweat-equity" provides that buy-in. How ownership of the accounts receivable are handled when one acquires equity or gives up equity are important issues to understand.

REAL ESTATE

Some physician groups own real estate. At other times, certain individual physicians may own real estate that the group uses or rents from the individuals. It is important to understand any such relationships.

LIABILITIES

Some physician groups borrow money for various purposes. Liabilities of the practice will of course impact the net revenue coming from the practice. In addition to defined liabilities, there are at times less well-defined liabilities such as deferred compensation. For example, there may be agreements to pay physicians large amounts on retirement, especially founders of a group or other senior members. It is important to be aware of these arrangements, which will impact the value of equity in a group and drain a significant amount of revenue that would otherwise be available to compensate the actively practicing physician group members. Another undefined liability may be "tail" insurance. Some physician groups prefund "tail" insurance. In other instances, it is a liability that must be paid as physicians leave practice.

SUMMARY

Large numbers of emergency physician practices are structured as independent groups holding exclusive contracts with the hospitals in which they practice. These groups often offer the possibility of an ownership interest to physicians who join the practice. Ownership generally offers more favorable treatment in terms of job security, income, and participation in management decisions. However, the value and cost of acquiring an equity interest vary significantly. It is important for physicians, in evaluating such opportunities, to understand each of the various forms of emergency medicine practice structure and to be able to assess the value and cost of acquiring an ownership interest in the practice.

5

MEDICAL MALPRACTICE INSURANCE

Editor's Note: Being covered by a professional liability policy that is written by a solid insurer and carries appropriate limits provides significant peace of mind for the practicing emergency physician. Your contract will undoubtedly address this issue. The following chapter explains the difference between "occurrence" and "claims-made" policies, as well as other common issues inherent in securing liability insurance.

During the past few decades, there has been a dramatic rise in professional liability claims asserted against members of the medical profession. An American Medical Association study from the 1950s found that only one physician in seven was sued for medical malpractice during the course of his or her professional career.[1] In contrast, most physicians who begin practice today can expect to face at least one such claim in their professional lifetime. Currently, each year, about 15 malpractice claims are filed for every 100 physicians; about 30% of those claims result in an insurance payment.[2,3] Various reasons for the increased number of claims have been suggested, including the heightened expectations of health care consumers, the expansion of tort doctrines and legislation that favor plaintiffs, the increased willingness of patients to pursue lawsuits against their physicians, the increased number of attorneys who are willing to bring malpractice lawsuits, and the increased availability of physicians who are willing to offer expert testimony on behalf of plaintiffs.

Along with the increase in the number of suits, the severity of claims has also increased, with the result that malpractice premiums now account for a substantial percentage of physicians' gross annual earnings from practice.[4]

(Compare with less than 1% in the 1950s and 1960s; some specialties, such as obstetrics, can have even higher insurance costs.) The Congressional Budget Office (CBO) reports that on average, premiums for all physicians nationwide rose by 15% between 2000 and 2002. Reportedly, that percentage is twice the increase in total health care spending. Nationally, certain specialties face greater increases than the average 15%; for instance, obstetricians experienced a 22% increase and internists and general surgeons faced a 33% increase in premiums.[5]

Medical malpractice liability insurance, once a minimal part of a physician's practice, has become an essential consideration for the practitioner. This chapter is designed to acquaint the physician with various aspects of professional liability insurance and to review in general the nature and purpose of medical malpractice insurance. Policies of insurance are all taken from basic forms and thus have many similarities among them. However, policies can be tailored to the needs of the insurer and the insured; therefore, each individual policy should be reviewed and analyzed carefully by the insured in consultation with an experienced broker or counsel to ensure the appropriate coverage is provided.

THE INSURANCE CONTRACT

All insurance contracts are governed by the terms of the written policy. Professional liability policies, like other liability policies, contain insuring agreements (a promise to pay or indemnify and to defend by the insurer), exclusions, conditions, and definitions. Also, some policies agree to cover attorney's cost up to a predefined limit during medical board representation. Although the wording of the coverage provision varies from company to company, a typical insuring clause reads as follows:

The company agrees:

Coverage A–Individual Professional Liability

(1) To pay on behalf of the insured all sums which the insured shall become obligated to pay by reason of the liability imposed upon him by law for damages resulting from any claim first made against the insured during the policy period and arising out of the performance of professional services for others in the insured's capacity as a physician, surgeon, or dentist and caused by any act, error or omission of the insured or any other person for whose acts the insured is legally liable.

(2) To defend the insured without limit of cost in any suit against the

foregoing specifications filed at any time, and to furnish any bond not exceeding in amount the minimum limit of this policy which may be incidentally necessary for such suits, for appeals or the release of attachments or garnishments; it being understood, however, that no law costs shall be incurred without the consent of the Company.

Coverage B–Partnership, Association, or Corporation Professional Liability

(1) To pay on behalf of the insured all sums which the insured shall become obligated to pay by reason of the liability imposed upon the insured by law for damages resulting from any claim first made against the insured during the policy period and arising out of the performance of professional medical services for others by any person for whose acts or omissions the professional partnership, association, or corporate insured is legally responsible.

(2) To defend the insured without limit of cost in any suit against the foregoing specifications filed at any time, and to furnish any bond not exceeding in amount the minimum limit of this policy which may be incidentally necessary for such suits, for appeals or the release of attachments or garnishments; it being understood, however, that no law costs shall be incurred without the consent of the Company.

Thus, the insurer agrees to defend its insured against any claim potentially covered by the policy. The defense obligation arises even when a claim of malpractice is false, fraudulent, unjust, or frivolous. Where a complaint alleges multiple causes of action against the professional, some covered and some not covered by the professional liability policy, the insurer has a duty to defend its insured against all claims. The duty to defend is very broad, but it is not unlimited. If a claim clearly falls outside of the scope of the policy, the insurer will not have to defend the action. For example, a malpractice insurer was not required to defend its insured physician where the plaintiff sought damages for alleged sexual assault, because intentional misconduct was specifically excluded under the policy.[6]

The insurer also agrees to indemnify or to pay on behalf of its insured any sums that the insured becomes legally obligated to pay as damages. The duty to defend is broader than the duty to indemnify. The duty to defend is determined from the facts alleged in the complaint. The duty to indemnify is determined from the facts proved at trial.

If an insurer believes coverage does not exist under the policy, it may defend under a reservation of rights and then seek judicial determination of the coverage issue. For example, if the complaint alleges both negligent and intentional misconduct, the insurer is required to defend the entire action. However, if the insured is ultimately found liable for damages arising out of intentional rather than merely negligent misconduct, the insurer may have no duty to indemnify or to pay those damages on behalf of the insured based on policy exclusions. In such cases, the interests of the company and those of the insured are adverse in certain respects and the insured is entitled to "conflict counsel," an attorney of the insured's choice who shall have the right to control the conduct of the litigation. By reason of the company's contractual obligation to furnish a defense, it must reimburse its insured for the reasonable cost of defending the action.[7]

THE INSURED

Physicians often practice as partnerships or as professional corporations. Some physicians are employees of hospitals, clinics, or other entities. It is important to determine who is insured under the policy. Those individuals and entities named on the "declarations page" of the policy will certainly be insured. If the named insured is a partnership, coverage generally extends to all partners and former partners to the extent of actions undertaken on behalf of the partnership. When the named insured is a professional corporation, coverage generally extends to shareholders, officers, and directors. Employees of the partnership or corporation may or may not be covered. Employee coverage can be purchased for an additional premium. If the physician is an employee, she must ascertain whether the employer will provide professional liability insurance and, if so, whether the coverage and policy limits are adequate. In all cases, it must be determined who will pay the premiums and deductible amount, if any, when a claim is filed.

Partners may be liable for the negligence of their partners. Further, physicians may be liable for the negligence of employees who assist the physician in providing professional services. Some policies exclude vicariously imposed liability, and the insurer is not obligated under the policy to the insured for his vicarious liability. The above-mentioned policy language provides coverage to the named insured not only for his own acts but also for injuries caused by anyone who acts under the direction, control, or supervision of the named insured. Thus, if a lawsuit were filed against a physician based on the negligence of her office nurse, coverage would exist. If the physician is in a partnership or professional corporation and/or employs others, he or she should obtain professional assistance at the time coverage is placed to ensure the policy provides coverage and liability limits commensurate with the potential exposure possible from the type of practice in which the physician is engaged.

WHAT IS COVERED: PROFESSIONAL SERVICES

Physicians' malpractice insurance typically covers insureds for all damage that flows from acts, errors, or omissions in the performance of "professional services." Professional services include conduct that requires the use of the physician's skills, knowledge, and training and/or conduct that occurs during the course of medical treatment. Professional liability policies cover the physician's affirmative negligence ("any act"), his failure to perform properly ("error"), and his failure to perform at all ("omission"). In addition to professional liability coverage, physician groups and self-employed practitioners usually will require other types of coverage, such as a comprehensive general liability policy to cover damages that occur in the ordinary course of business (e.g., where a patient is injured when she slips and falls on a wet floor in the physician's waiting area). A discussion of the variety of coverage available is beyond the scope of this chapter, but it is important to remember that professional liability insurance supplements rather than replaces more common types of insurance.

Sometimes a question exists as to whether conduct constitutes professional service so as to be covered by the insured's professional liability policy.[8] In the context of medical malpractice insurance, this problem often arises in situations that involve allegations of defamation or sexual misconduct. For instance, if a physician makes statements to a local newspaper regarding a patient's level of intoxication, do those statements constitute professional service? At least one court said yes, reasoning that the statements arose from the physician's provision of medical treatment.[9] On the other hand, a physician's statements to a newspaper that certain colleagues were performing unnecessary and improper operations were found not to have been made in the course of rendering professional services, resulting in no coverage when the physician was sued for defamation.[10] If a patient sues her psychiatrist for negligence and assault and battery after the two become sexually involved during the course of treatment, does the alleged conduct involve the provision of professional services? Many courts have found that an insured physician's sexual relations with a patient are separate and distinct from medical treatment (resulting in no coverage),[11] whereas a minority have found that the sexual relationship between the insured and the patient is so intertwined with treatment that the case is best viewed as one of ordinary negligence (resulting in coverage).[12]

WHAT IS NOT COVERED: EXCLUSIONS

Assuming that the conduct that resulted in the complaint does fall within the realm of professional services, coverage may be denied based on exclusions in the policy. Most professional liability policies exclude coverage for claims-made by an entity in which the insured has an ownership interest (to discourage improper collusion). In general, policies exclude coverage for liability assumed by the insured under contract or under an indemnity agreement. Many policies include provisions that exclude coverage for "moral hazards." Such exclusions apply to claims based on intentional misconduct, fraud, dishonesty, or criminal acts. Many policies exclude coverage for punitive damages; "punitive damages" are monetary damages in excess of actual damages and are intended to punish and deter wrongdoers. (Punitive damages are generally recoverable by a malpractice plaintiff only when the malpractice is accompanied by aggravating circumstances, such as when the defendant knew or should have known the conduct would probably cause injury. Even gross negligence will not usually result in an award of punitive damages. Some states have enacted statutes that specifically bar the award of punitive damages in medical malpractice cases.) Even where "moral hazards" or punitive damages are not excluded under the policy, courts may uphold an insurer's refusal to pay such damages on behalf of the insured based on considerations of public policy (if one can insure himself against punishment, there is no disincentive to wrongdoing).

The insured must be cognizant of the particular provisions of her policy to avoid an unexpected failure of coverage. For example, where a medical malpractice policy excluded coverage if the insured did not notify the insurer in writing of illness or disability that potentially impaired the insured's ability to practice medicine, there was no coverage as to claims that arose after the defendant physician was aware he had a substance abuse problem.[13]

CONDITIONS/DUTIES OF THE PARTIES

All liability policies impose specified duties, known as "conditions," on the insurer and the insured. In general, the insured is required to provide written notice of an occurrence, claim, or suit either immediately or as soon as reasonably possible. Thus, when an insured is served with a summons and complaint, the insured must promptly notify the insurance carrier. Some notice provisions require notice in writing. Other provisions would be met if oral notice is given. Under certain circumstances, an insured's failure to immediately notify his carrier of a claim may result in the loss of coverage.[14] The insured is obligated to cooperate with the insurer, which includes assisting the carrier in its investigation, pursuing rights against other parties, and attending hearings and trials as required. The insurer is obligated to pay any judgment to the extent of coverage under the policy, regardless of the financial condition of the insured. The insurer also has a duty to provide reasonable notice and must show reasonable diligence in its requests for cooperation. The insurer must include in its policy a cancellation provision setting out the manner in which the policy may be terminated or simply not renewed. Again, reasonable notice is required. Both parties to the insurance contract owe a duty of good faith and fair dealing.

TYPES OF COVERAGE

OCCURRENCE-BASED POLICIES

Most general liability policies are "occurrence based." Occurrence-based policies provide coverage if the occurrence (the discernable event or events that caused injury) happens during the policy period, regardless of when the claim is filed. However, occurrence-based policies are inherently problematic in medical malpractice claims. For example, if treatment extends over a period of time, it may be unclear when the occurrence took place. It may be unclear as to whether the act or the harm constitutes the occurrence. For instance, the emergency physician fails to diagnose appendicitis on Sunday while policy A is in effect. The patient's appendix ruptures on Tuesday while policy B is in effect. Which policy should cover the medical malpractice claim? In one case, an insurer claimed that injuries to an epileptic child after the insured physician discontinued antiseizure medications and the patient experienced a grand mal seizure were covered by the insured's policy with $200,000 limits in effect at the time of the physician's decision, rather than the subsequent policy with $1 million limits in effect at the time of the convulsion. The court disagreed, construing the ambiguity in the policy as to what constituted the "occurrence" in favor of the insured.[15]

Occurrence-based professional liability policies create significant underwriting problems because of the long or open "tail" exposure that results. As one court noted:

> "When the 'event' intended to be covered cannot easily be fixed and the liability for the consequent injury extends long into the future, often well

after expiration of the policy, considerations of inflation, upward spiraling jury verdicts, and legislative and judicial adoption of newly developing concepts of tort law might mean that actuarial factors, including fixing premium rates and establishing adequate reserves, are highly speculative. The result, logically, is the establishment of a premium rate schedule sufficiently high to accommodate 'worst scenario' jury verdicts returned years after the error, omission, or negligent act."[16]

CLAIMS-MADE POLICIES

As a result of the above-mentioned difficulties, most professional liability policies are now written on a "claims-made" basis. Claims-made policies provide coverage for claims first made against an insured during the policy period. A claim is an assertion by a third party against the insured. It is not notice to the insurer. Accordingly, if Dr. Jones is served with a summons and complaint on the last day of a claims-made policy period and notifies her carrier the day after the policy expires, coverage will exist. Indeed, unless the policy expressly states that the insured must actually receive notice of the claim when it is first asserted, the filing of a lawsuit triggers the claims-made policy even though the insured does not learn of it until after the policy has expired.[17] Thus, if the plaintiff files a lawsuit against Dr. Jones on the last day of the policy but the physician is not served with the summons and complaint until 2 months after the expiration of the policy, coverage will nonetheless exist. Of course, not every situation is so clear cut. What types of communications to the insured, short of the filing of a lawsuit, constitute a "claim"? Some policies define the word "claim" as "a demand received by the insured for money or services." In the absence of a specific definition, the question may become one for the courts. In one Illinois decision, a court found an insured hospital was put on notice of a claim when a well known plaintiff's personal injury attorney requested medical records concerning the birth of a severely handicapped infant.[18]

Claims-made policies permit the professional to have coverage with liability limits that mirror current liability exposure. Claims-made policies also enable the carrier to better predict the limits of its exposure and to more accurately estimate the premium schedule required to accommodate the risk. However, claims-made policies are not without certain disadvantages. A pure claims-made policy covers the loss for any claims-made against the insured during the policy period regardless of the date of the conduct in question or the date of the injury claimed. This scenario obviously presents a moral hazard in that if an insured had reason to know that a claim would be asserted against him and if he was uninsured at the time of the negligence, he could still purchase a claims-made policy, notify the insurer of his negligence, and then seek coverage when the claim is asserted against him during the policy period. Accordingly, most policies provide a "prior acts" clause, or "retroactive date," that excludes from coverage acts and omissions that precede the date of inception of the first claims-made policy. Most policies also include a provision to the effect that acts, errors, or omissions of the insured that occur before the inception of the policy but within the retroactive period specified will be covered only if (1) the insured is unaware of any facts or circumstances that a professional duty was breached or that may reasonably give rise to a claim and (2) no other policy covers the claim.

GAPS IN COVERAGE

Although an act, error, or omission during the policy period may eventually lead to a claim, if the claim is not made until after the policy has expired, the insurer in general will not be obligated to defend or indemnify the insured. Thus, gaps in coverage can exist. For example, Dr. Jones is covered by a claims-made policy, "A," that ends on December 31. Starting January 1, Dr. Jones is covered by an occurrence-based policy, "B." If Dr. Jones commits a negligent act on December 30 and is sued on January 15, she will not be covered under either policy because the claim was not made until policy A had expired and the negligent act occurred before policy B took effect. Similarly, if Dr. Jones retires from practice or if her claims-made policy is canceled or not renewed, exposure remains for claims made against her after expiration of the policy. Even a change from one claims-made policy with one insurance company to another with another company can result in a gap in coverage relative to incidents that took place under the expired policy but for which a claim is asserted only after the new policy takes effect.

HYBRID POLICIES

Some insurers write hybrid claims-made/reporting policies that require that claims first be made against the insured during the policy period and that notice of the claim be given to the insurer carrier during the policy period. Based on this language, if a claim is asserted against an insured physician on the last effective day of the policy and if the physician does not notify the carrier until the next day, at which point the policy is no longer in force, the claim is uninsured. For obvious reasons, such a policy should be avoided.

"Tail" Coverage

When claims-made coverage is discontinued, for whatever reason, the physician must protect herself by purchasing "tail" endorsements. "Tail" endorsement, or extended discovery period coverage, may be part of the terms of the policy itself or may be purchased separately (usually within a short period of time after the policy expires) to extend the policy (usually for a period of 3 years). "Tail" endorsements cover claims-made after the expiration of the claims-made policy when the act, error, or omission occurred before expiration of the last claims-made policy. When an insured elects not to purchase optional "tail" coverage, he will not be heard to complain that the policy was unfair or against public policy if he is uninsured for a later reported claim.[19]

Generally, "tail" coverage rates are tied directly to malpractice rates, such that as malpractice insurance premiums increase so do "tail" coverage rates. As of August 2004, "tail" coverage has been reported as costing 150% to 200% of the price of a mature claims-made policy. The exact price, of course, depends on where a physician practices and the particular medical specialty. By example, an internist in the Chicago area, paying $41,000 for a mature claims-made policy, would pay about $62,000 for "tail" coverage; an obstetrician in Chicago might be forced to pay a bill around $229,000.[20] Other sources estimate typical "tail" coverage costs at up to two and one-half times the amount of the past year's premium. Thus, a physician who paid $100,000 during his last year of practice would be required to pay $250,000 within a month of retirement, in order to maintain liability coverage.[21] Doctors who switch malpractice carriers at the end of the year are financially the hardest hit, as they have already paid their yearly premiums and are then required to pay the even higher amount for "tail" coverage.

Physicians should be aware that many carriers provide complimentary extended "tail" coverage at retirement if the practitioner has been an insured for a specified period of time. (Of course, the cost of that "tail" coverage is then spread among the practicing physicians in the similar specialty.)

Discovery Clause

The physician who seeks to purchase or renew a claims-made policy is usually required to complete an application that seeks information regarding the professional's knowledge of facts or circumstances that might give rise to a claim. Of course, this can result in a "no win" situation. If the physician knows such facts but does not reveal them and later a claim is made arising out of those facts during the term of the new policy, the insured will be accused of misrepresentation. On the other hand, if the physician reveals facts that might result in a claim, the policy will be issued with an endorsement that excludes coverage for that occurrence.

Fortunately, most claims-made policies include a "discovery" clause that provides if the insured becomes aware, during the period of a claims-made policy, of circumstances that may result in a claim (e.g., after a patient's death from complications of postoperative infection, the surgeon learns that the sponge count was inaccurate) and the insured gives notice of her error or the possible claim to the insurer during the term of the policy, a claim asserted after the policy expires is deemed to be a claim made during the policy period (at the time notice was given to the insurer). Despite the fear of increased premiums, rejection, cancellation, or nonrenewal, an insured is best advised to notify her claims-made carrier immediately on learning of a significant error or possible claim.

DEDUCTIBLES AND POLICY LIMITS

Most medical malpractice policies contain deductibles that apply to indemnity as well as to defense costs. The deductible usually applies on a "per-claim" basis. In addition, policies commonly contain both individual and "aggregate" limits. Individual limit is generally defined as the maximum amount payable for injuries sustained by any one patient, and aggregate refers to the total amount the policy will cover for all claims or suits reported during the policy year period.

Currently, individual physician policies typically provide policy limits of $1 million per person and $3 million in the aggregate.[22] The majority of hospital bylaws require that physicians carry at least $1 million to $3 million in coverage to maintain medical staff privileges. Some policies, known as "diminishing limits policies," include the costs of defense in the limits. Such policies are of significantly lower value to the insured because defense costs will continually reduce the net limit available for damages. Of course, premiums for diminishing limits policies are usually lower than those for cost exclusive policies.

Under certain circumstances, an issue may arise as to whether the per-claim limit or the aggregate limit applies. For example, in medical malpractice claims, family members of the injured patient may have derivative injuries, such as attendant financial responsibilities or loss of consortium. Courts have been inconsistent as to whether family members' injuries constitute part of the patient's claim or whether they are separate claims so as to trigger aggregate limits of the policy.[23] Similarly, there may separate and distinct acts of negligence to the same patient. For instance, a physician was insured under two successive professional liability policies. In the first policy period, the physician negligently prescribed medications. During the second policy period, the physician negligently failed to monitor the patient's response to the combination of drugs. As a result of adverse drug interactions, the patient experienced a series of complications, which were also negligently treated by the physician. The carrier maintained that only one policy applied and that coverage extended only to the individual limits of liability. The court disagreed, finding that both policies applied and that separate and distinct acts of negligence during the second policy period triggered the aggregate limit. Such cases are very fact specific, and as a general rule, courts tend to favor insureds in analyzing policy limit and deductible issues.

In some situations, two or more policies may apply in covering the same insured for the same loss. Insurance policies use "other insurance" clauses to determine which of several insurers assumes primary or excess liability for the claim. Some policies include a "pro rata" clause that provides the policy will pay benefits at the ration of its limits to the final judgment. Some policies are designated as "excess" to any other policies, attempting to limit liability to amounts in excess of other insurer's coverage. Some policies contain an "escape" clause that attempts to negate liability under the policy for any claim for which the insured is entitled to any indemnity under any other insurance. Courts generally look to the policy language to determine priority and proportion of payment by the various carriers.

The selection of appropriate policy limits is essential to ensure proper coverage. Adequate insurance is generally the amount typically held by other physicians in your area and specialty. However, many factors will affect the coverage and liability limits required by the physician. For example, where the physician is employed by an entity with separate coverage, the employer may be responsible for a judgment against the physician in excess of the physician's policy limits and the physician may elect to pay lower premiums for relatively lower liability limits. On the other hand, if the physician is an independent contractor, a judgment in excess of policy limits may place personal assets at risk.

Some have questioned whether a physician, by choosing to pay higher premiums or deductibles for higher policy limits, ultimately only increases the value of a claim by increasing the amount recoverable from the physician's insurer.[24] Plaintiffs' attorneys often purposely demand a defendant physician's policy limits to settle. This tactic puts pressure on the relationship between the insured and insurer by exploiting the point at which their interests might diverge. For example, an insurer who believes there is a good defense may find no economic incentive to settle for the policy's limits, beyond which the insurer has no further liability to indemnify the insured under the policy. On the other hand, a physician confronted with a policy limit demand may desire settlement to avoid the possibility of personal liability in the event of an adverse judgment in excess of coverage.

Medical malpractice insurance is a cost of doing business, nothing more or less. Determining which of many and complex available options to pursue is one aspect of your practice that mandates garnering the advice of experts. A good rule of thumb, however, is that an increased premium for adequate coverage and limits is a far better alternative than an uncovered or inadequately covered lawsuit for medical malpractice.

SETTLEMENT

Standard provisions in insurance contracts give the insurer control over the defense of any claim against the insured, including the right to decide whether to settle a case. The insurer owes a fiduciary duty to protect the interests of its insured. The insurer's right to control the litigation creates an implied duty on the part of the insurer not to gamble with the insured's money by foregoing reasonable opportunity to settle on terms that protect the insured from judgment in excess of policy limits.[25] The duty to settle is triggered by the existence of a claim within the scope of coverage, a settlement demand that would be acceptable to the ordinarily prudent insurer, and the demand must be within policy limits. The insurer is obligated to make a thorough investigation of the claim against its insured. The insurer need not settle with the claimant if, on the basis of this investigation, it determines that there is a reasonable likelihood the insured will prevail at trial.

When an insurer unreasonably fails to settle an action within policy limits, thereby exposing the insured to personal liability in excess of that amount, the insured may seek to recover against the insurer. For instance, an insurer was found liable for a judgment in excess of policy limits against its insured where the insurer acted negligently and in bad faith in refusing to settle a medical malpractice case. The case against the insured physician was strong, the insured was exposed to financial risk beyond the coverage provided by the policy, the insurer failed to keep the insured adequately informed regarding settlement negotiations, and there was evidence that the insurer rejected the advice of the insured's attorney.[26]

Traditionally, in recognition of the impact of settlement on a physician's professional reputation, most medical malpractice policies contain a clause providing that the insured must consent to any settlement. Consent provisions usually appear in the coverage and liability limit portions of the insurance policy. Some policies, however, reserve exclusively to the insurer the right to decide whether to settle a claim. These policies are generally offered at a slight premium reduction and courts typically reject a physician's attempt to block settlement if there is a "no consent" clause in the policy.[27]

Where the physician enjoys the right of consent, an insurer may be liable if it settles the case against the wishes of the insured.[28] When deciding whether to consent to settlement, the physician must take into consideration the possibility of an adverse jury verdict greatly in excess of policy limits. Moreover, some policies with consent clauses seek to discourage the insured from gambling with insurance company money by including a proviso that if the insured refuses to consent to settle and a judgment comes back against the insured, the insurer is not liable for any amount over the amount for which the case could have been settled had the insured consented. Although settling may make economic sense, the settlement usually must be reported to the physician's hospital, HMOs, state licensing boards and the National Practitioner Data bank. Thus, there may exist reasons, outside of finances, that make settling a poor choice for a physician with a good defense.

REFERENCES

1. Opinion survey on medical malpractice. JAMA 1957; 164.
2. Thorpe, Kenneth E. *The Medical Malpractice "Crisis": Recent Trends and the Impact of State Tort Reforms.* Presented at the Council on Health Care Economics and Policy conference, Medical Malpractice in Crisis: Health Care Policy Options, Washington, D.C., March 3, 2003.
3. CBO calculations based on data from the Physician Insurers Association of America.
4. Sloan, Bovbjerg, and Githens (1991). *Insuring Medical Malpractice.* New York, Oxford University press.
5. CBO. *Limiting Tort Liability for Medical Malpractice,* at http://www.cbo.gov/showdoc.cfm?index=4968&sequence=0. Accessed October 26, 2004.
6. *Prior v. South Carolina Medical Malpractice Lab. Ins. Joint Underwriting Assoc.,* 407 S.E.2d 655 (S.C. Ct. App. 1991).
7. *Maryland Casualty Company v. Peppers,* 64 Ill.2d 187, 355 N.E.2d 24 (1976).
8. For example, a radiologist sought coverage under his professional liability policy where the radiologist's negligent pulling of a radioactive protective cart resulted in the cart striking and injuring a nurse. Although the radiologist was pulling the cart to render professional care to a patient, the service was not provided by the radiologist in the practice of his profession as a physician; thus the claim was not covered by the policy. *Hartford Cas. Ins. Co. v. Shehala,* 427 F.Supp. 336, reversed and remanded, 577 F.2d 746 (N.D.Ill. 1977).
9. *Mellow v. Medical Malpractice Joint Underwriting Association,* 567 A.2d 367 (R.I. 1989).
10. *Buckner v. Physicians Protective Trust Fund,* 376 So.2d 461 (Fla.App. 1979).
11. See, for example, *New Mexico Physicians Mutual Liability Insurance Co. v. LaMure,* 116 N.M. 92, 860 P.2d 734 (1993); *Snyder v. Major,* 818 F.Supp. 68 (S.D.N.Y. 1993); *Cluett v. Medical Protective Co.,* 829 S.W.2d 822 (Tex.App. 1992); *St. Paul Insurance Co. v. Cromeans,* 771 F.Supp. 349 (N.D.Ala. 1991); *Hartogs v. Employers Mutual Liability Insurance Co.,* 89 Misc.2d 468, 391 N.Y.
12. See, for example, *Vetter v. Subotnik,* 844 F.Supp. 1352 (D. Minn. 1992) (reasoning psychiatrist's departure from standards or therapeutic practice set in motion chain of events leading up to injury); *St. Paul Fire & Marine Insurance Co. v. Torpoco,* 879 S.W.2d 831 (Tenn. 1994); *St. Paul Fire & Marine Insurance Co. v. Shernow,* 222 Conn. 823, 610 A.2d 1281 (1992);

Dillon v. Callaway, 609 N.E.2d 424 (Ind.App. 1993).

13. *Illinois State Medical Ins. Services, Inc. v. Cichon,* 258 Ill.App.3d 803, 629 N.E.2d 822 (3ʳᵈ Dist. 1994).

14. See for example, *Prior v. South Carolina Medical Malpractice Lab. Ins. Joint Underwriting Assoc.,* 407 S.E.2d 655 (S.C. Ct. App. 1991) (insurer had no duty to defend where insured physician failed to notify his malpractice insurer of patient's complaint until 21 months after first becoming aware of it); *Montgomery v. Professional Mut. Ins. Co.,* 611 F.2d 818 (10ᵗʰ Cir. 1980) (Insured physician could not recover from his malpractice liability carrier for its failure to defend him where he failed to inform insurer of claim against him until more than 2 years after he had been served in the action). But see *Public Serv. Mut. Ins. Co. v. Goldfarb,* 53 N.Y.2d 392, 425 N.E.2d 810 (1981) (Dentist's professional liability policy required that he notify insurer as soon as possible "in the event of an accident, unusual occurrence or receiving notice of claim or suit." Court found dentist's failure to notify insurer on institution of disciplinary proceedings and criminal action against him could not be characterized as "unusual occurrences" given ambiguity of policy language, thus, when dentist immediately notified insurer upon being served with process in a civil suit, insurer was required to defend).

15. *Rozenfeld v. Medical Protective Co.,* 73 F.3d 154 (C.A.7 (Ill.) 1996).

16. *Stine v. Continental Cas. Co.,* 419 Mich. 89, 349 N.W.2d 127 (1984).

17. *Employers Reinsurance Corp. v. Phoenix Insurance Co.,* 186 Cal.App.3d 545, 230 Cal.Rptr. 792 (1ˢᵗ Dist. 1986).

18. *American Continental Insurance Co. V. Marion Memorial Hospital,* 773 F.Supp. 1148 (S.D.ILL. 1991). But see *Columbia Casualty Co. v. Columbia Hospital for Women,* 633 F.Supp. 697 (D.D.C. 1986) (attorney's letter to hospital requesting medical records was not a claim).

19. See, for example, *Hickox v. Stover,* 551 So.2d 259 (Ala. 1989).

20. Murray, Dennis (2004). "Medical Liability: The Scary Truth About Tail Coverage." *Urol Times,* August 15, p. 34.

21. Gunnar, William P. (2004). "Is There an Acceptable Answer to Rising Medical Malpractice Premiums?" *Ann Health Law.* 13:465, 470.

22. Rice, Berkeley (2004). "How High Now?" *Med. E,* January 9, p. 57; Jackiw, Christina O. (2004). "The Current Medical Liability Insurance Crisis: An Overview of the Problem." *Ann Health Law.* 13:505, 512 (2004).

23. See, for example, *Guaranty Nat'l Ins. Co. v. North River Ins. Co.,* 909 F.2d 133 (5ᵗʰ Cir. 1990) (A malpractice action that included claims for bodily injury to the patient and loss of consortium on the part of the patient's

spouse constituted one claim for purposes of the policy and the single claim limit and not the aggregate claim limit applied); *Thompson v. St. Paul Fire & Marine Ins. Co.*, 702 P.2d 840 (Utah 1985)(same). But see *Pinheiro v. Medical Malpractice Joint Underwriting Assoc. of Mass.*, 547 N.E.2d 49 (Mass. 1989) (An insured physician was sued for malpractice by a patient and for loss of consortium by the patient's family members. The court rejected the insurer's contention that because the family members' injuries were derivative in nature, all claims amounted to only one claim under the policy. The court, reasoning that the policy language, "injury to any one person," was broad enough to include loss of consortium injuries, construed the ambiguity in the policy in favor of the insured and held that the aggregate limit applied).

24. Jerry, Robert, and Richmond, Douglas (2004). The insurance aspects of damages. J Disp Resol 106, 114.
25. *Twin city Fire Ins. Co. v. Country Mut. Ins. Co.*, 23 F.3d 1175 (C.A.7 (Ill.) 1994); *Transport Ins. Co., Inc. v. Post Exp. Co., Inc.*, 138 F.3d 1189.
26. *Insurance Co. of North America v. Medical Protective Co.*, 768 F.2d 315 (C.A. 10 (Kan.) 1985).
27. Johnson, Lee J. (2002). "If an Insurer Insists on Settling." *Med Econ* July 11, p. 96.
28. See, for example, *Brion v. Vigilant Ins. Co.*, 651 S.W.2d 183 (Mo. Ct. App. 1983); *Lieberman v. Employers Insurance of Wausau*, 84 N.J. 325, 419 A.2d 417 (1980).

6

EMPLOYEE VERSUS INDEPENDENT CONTRACTOR

Editor's Note: Whether you work as an employee or an independent contractor will affect your ability to deduct various business-related expenses on your income tax. It will also affect your potential tort liability and job security. Although the IRS seems to favor employee status for emergency physicians, it is still possible to practice as an independent contractor. However, improperly constructed independent contractor arrangements can result in expensive IRS audits. The following chapter should serve as a primer on this subject, but expert legal counsel is a must if you pursue the independent contractor route.

At the culmination of your job search, you will be asked to sign a contract. In all probability, the prospective hospital or physician group will present a form contract from which they are reluctant to deviate. The primary purpose of this chapter is not, therefore, to assist you in negotiating a contract but rather to provide you with a basic understanding of contract options and to guide your inquiry when considering alternative job opportunities. You must examine yourself, your personality, and your strengths and weaknesses.

You may be best served by a classic contract of employment, a classic contract as an independent contractor, or something in between. Each form of contract has significant advantages and disadvantages.

To fully evaluate which arrangement will best fit your needs and wants, do not rely solely on written materials. Armed with a basic understanding of the different options, engage in detailed discussions with practicing emergency physicians who operate under a variety of contractual arrangements. Ask questions about the perceived pros and cons of each arrangement. It may be helpful to discuss alternatives with an accountant to evaluate bookkeeping and tax consequences of potential arrangements. Discussions with legal counsel experienced in health care law and physician contracting may be helpful long before you consider an actual proposed contract.

DOES IT REALLY MATTER WHETHER YOU ARE AN EMPLOYEE OR INDEPENDENT CONTRACTOR?

The specific details of your contract may be much more important to you than your designation as a "employee" or "independent contractor." However, the designation becomes important in several respects, including:

- Tax liabilities, deductions, and payments
- Tort liability
- Access to rights afforded by law to employees but not to independent contractors

WHAT IS THE DIFFERENCE?

IT IS AN ISSUE OF CONTROL

Both employees and independent contractors perform work for another person or entity. *If that entity has the right to control the manner in which the work is performed, the worker is an employee. The worker is an independent contractor if the worker controls the manner in which the work is to be performed.* A simple nonmedical example might be helpful.

USE THE EXAMPLE OF A GARDENER

When your estate has outgrown your capacity to tend the gardens, you may decide it is time to hire someone to do the work for you. You have two options:

- Hire someone as an employee.
- Retain an independent contractor.

If you simply want the job done but care little about the details, you might find an independent contractor who would agree to keep the estate in a condition of perpetual splendor as specified in the contract. However, the manner in which that is accomplished is left to the contractor. He can do all of the work himself, he can hire others to do the work, he can work quickly or slowly, many hours or few, and he can use old equipment or new. It matters not so long as the objective is accomplished. If you want greater control of the details of how the work is performed, you may prefer to hire an employee. The employee can be told exactly when to work, when to take breaks, the type of equipment to use, exactly when to perform specific jobs, and so on. Typically, the employee would be paid an hourly wage, whereas the independent contractor would more likely receive a flat fee.

You, the landowner, may want the control that goes along with an employment relationship but you may not want the responsibility. As an employer, you would assume significant bookkeeping and payroll responsibilities to meet your obligations to the IRS. You would be compelled to comply with a mystifying array of state and federal laws and regulations that pertain to the duties of an employer.

From the gardener's perspective, the restraints associated with employment are at least in part compensated for by its benefits. The independent contractor's freedom from control carries significant burdens and risks.

EMPLOYMENT VERSUS INDEPENDENT CONTRACTOR FOR THE EMERGENCY PHYSICIAN

Hospitals are free to contract with individual physicians as employees or independent contractors. In practice, most hospitals either:

- Hire individual physicians as employees or
- Contract with an emergency physician group that provides services through individual physicians who are independent contractors or employees. A physician may be deemed an employee of a physician group even when the group has valid independent contractor agreements with one or more hospitals. A group may be given great freedom over how it provides emergency services to a hospital yet exert significant control over individual physician providers.

IRS INTEREST AND IMPACT

The IRS favors employment contracts for two reasons:

- It is easier for the IRS to monitor and collect taxes from a relatively smaller number of employers than from a larger number of independent contractors.

• Independent contractors are thought to take larger tax deductions and therefore generate less tax revenue. The actual tax savings vary among individuals. Some physicians aggressively pursue deductions for business related expenses such as travel, automobile, and so on, whereas others take minimal advantage. Most emergency physicians who work as independent contractors will realize less than $7,500 per year in tax savings.

The IRS uses approximately 20 criteria by which to determine whether an individual is an employee or an independent contractor. Each criterion relates to a component of the working relationship that may reflect the control by an entity over the individual worker. Those indicators of control are then evaluated, on balance, to determine whether the contract, regardless of its title, establishes an employment relationship. Unfortunately, there is no precise formula for that determination. Court decisions provide basic guidelines, but because the facts vary considerably in each case, one cannot always predict whether a specific agreement will withstand IRS scrutiny. The likelihood of a specific contractual agreement being audited by the IRS is not great. However, the physician should be aware that an adverse decision from an audit could result in fines and penalties even though all parties to the contract attempted to comply with the tax codes and regulations. A tax audit of an independent contractor agreement could result in the IRS recharacterizing the relationship as one of employment. As a consequence, the IRS may seek back taxes (with interest and penalties) from the "employer" for failing to withhold payroll tax. In addition, if you are recharacterized as an employee, your previous deductions to your retirement plan may be held as invalid, resulting in back taxes with interest and penalties that are due.

The relevant indicia of control vary from business to business. Some of the most significant IRS criteria applicable to emergency medicine agreements are:

1. Exclusivity: An individual who works exclusively for one group or hospital is subject to much greater control than one who provides services to several entities. A full-time arrangement, especially if mandated by contract, strongly suggests the type of control generally present in an employee/employer relationship.

2. Flexibility of Shift Hours: Efficient operation of an emergency department limits the extent to which individual physicians can control their work hours. However, within those restraints, hospitals or groups may provide a certain degree of independence by permitting physicians to switch shifts,

refuse assignments (within reason), and decline set hours. Flexibility suggests independence.

3. Method of Payment
   a. Income: Payment methods that resemble a salary are indicative of an employment relationship. Compensation based on hours or shifts worked suggests independence but is not conclusive.
   b. Business-related expenses: Payment or reimbursement of an individual's business-related expenses suggests an employee/employer relationship. One who is reimbursed for expenses of continuing medical education, travel, medical malpractice insurance, disability insurance, professional dues, and memberships may have a difficult time convincing the IRS that he or she is not an employee.

4. Method of Performance: An employer can dictate, with exactitude, how an employee is to complete an assigned task or duty. Independent contractors have greater flexibility over how they accomplish their contractual obligations. However, most employment and independent contractor agreements require individuals to comply with hospital bylaws and departmental rules. They may also require compliance with clinical protocols or practice guidelines. Such control probably does not invalidate the independent contractor status so long as it is not inflexible or inconsistent with the practices of most board-certified emergency physicians and is implemented for the public good rather than for institutional convenience.

5. Integration: A physician who becomes internally integrated into the day to day administrative functions of a group or hospital loses some degree of independence. That is seldom a problem for physicians fresh from training. However, administrative responsibilities often increase with age and experience. Contracts that require physicians to provide administrative services at the whim of the hospital or group may jeopardize independent contractor status.

6. Discharge and Termination: Independent contractors are obligated to meet contractual obligations and nothing more. Employees, on the other hand, are generally subject to termination for reasons separate and apart from the specific performance of their responsibilities. For example, employees may be dismissed for having a poor attitude, for being insubordinate,

or for myriad reasons that are not directly tied to specific performance. Contracts that allow non-performance-based discharge reflect considerable control through the threat of discharge or early termination. Conversely, an individual physician who is free to quit without consequence of legal liability is not as independent as he or she may believe. In fact, the ability to quit with impunity suggests an employment relationship. An employee is usually free to quit with little or no notice and has no independent contractual obligation to fulfill. An independent contractor must meet contractual obligations despite personal preferences.

Some IRS indicia used to evaluate other business relationships have little application here because of the inherent nature of the business of providing emergency medical services. When evaluating other types of business relationships, the IRS may find a requirement of personal performance to be a strong indicator of employment. Personal performance is not a significant criterion for evaluating emergency medicine contracts. Very few emergency physicians can meet their obligations by hiring others or subcontracting the work, because hospitals are required by law to credential physicians for the protection of the public. Courts are not likely to discourage such controlling behavior that is essential to the public good.

Because of IRS scrutiny, independent contractor agreements often verbosely exclaim the independence of the physician. However, the expressed independence may not accurately depict the true relationship between the parties. It is therefore essential to look beyond the written word when considering a prospective opportunity. There is no substitute for candid discussions with individuals who have, for some time, been operating under the basic agreement you are considering.

TORT LIABILITY

Employers are legally liable for the conduct of their employees. Except as explained later (apparent agency), a hospital or group is not legally responsible for the conduct of an independent contractor. The determination of whether one is an independent contractor or employee for the purpose of establishing tort liability is made by trial and appellate courts based on the common law of individual states (*common law* is the law established by judges on a case-to-case basis, as opposed to *statutory law*, which is created by legislators, or *regulatory law*, which is created by government administrative bodies). In determining whether a physician is an employer or independent contractor, state courts are also interested in the issue of control. Using a variety of criteria, they explore available evidence to determine whether the hospital or group exercised the type of control over the individual that should make them responsible for his or her conduct. Trial courts, unlike the IRS, are often woefully ignorant of the complexity of business relationships in the health care field. Also unlike the IRS, trial courts are often confronted by profoundly needy individuals seeking deep pocket sources for recovery. In examining the identical arrangement, a state court and the IRS may reach opposite conclusions with respect to whether a physician is an employee or independent contractor. Judges in one state may reach different conclusions from judges in other states. Even within the same state, different judges may reach different conclusions.

Some states have attempted to avoid the issue by declaring that the actual arrangement between the physician and group or hospital is not as important as the apparent arrangement. They have held that emergency physicians, regardless of their actual relationship, may be the apparent agents of the facility at which they provide services. This analysis shifts the focus from the agreement between the physician and the institution to the perception of the health care recipient.

Unfortunately, the law of apparent agency is muddled, varies tremendously among the states, and is in constant flux.

The individual physician is better protected from personal financial responsibility if he or she is found to be an employee or apparent agent. If found to be an independent contractor, the physician is protected only to the extent of his or her malpractice liability insurance. It is probably futile for an individual physician to engage in the exercise of predicting how a future court will interpret what purports to be an independent contractor agreement. Adequate personal malpractice insurance is a must. Determining what is "adequate" depends on many factors, including your jurisdiction and your personal financial condition. A detailed discussion of that issue is beyond the scope of this chapter.

RIGHTS SPECIFIC TO EMPLOYEES

State, federal, and common laws provide certain protections to employees that do not apply to independent contractors. As an independent contractor, you will not be able to derive the potential benefit of the following:

- Workers' Compensation benefits
- Unemployment compensation
- Federal labor laws regarding union activities

- Equal Pay Act prohibiting gender pay discrimination
- Age employment discrimination laws
- Family Medical Leave Act
- Certain protections afforded by the Americans with Disabilities Act
- Protection afforded to complainants under OSHA
- Common law protections against retaliatory discharge
- Retirement protection laws
- Employee benefit packages

KEY ELEMENTS IN BOTH FORMS OF CONTRACT

Regardless of which form of contract you are considering, you should pay particular attention to the following issues:

1. Introductory Clauses, Preambles, Whereas Clauses, and so on:
   Most contracts contain preliminary language that identify the parties and explain the general purpose of the contract. Do not be misled by assurances that the wording in such provisions is not significant or unenforceable. Preamble language is sometimes relied on strongly by courts to determine the intent of the parties. It is also sometimes used by third parties such as malpractice litigants, the IRS, JCAHO, or other regulatory bodies. Nonessential language should be avoided, as should hyperbole and "feel good" language. Never promise to meet higher standards of care than the law requires or make any promises that you cannot or do not intend to keep. Preamble language can undermine the independence established in the body of the contract.

2. Compensation: The compensation formula is usually simpler for employees than for independent contractors. Employees may be paid by shift, by hour, by month, or by year. Occasionally, employment contracts contain bonus provisions or incentives. Compensation plans for independent contractors are more variable and sometimes quite complex. They are more likely to be tied to production and are based on complex formulas that relate to hours, shifts, billings, collections, and so on. When comparing contracts, do not overestimate the tax advantages available to the independent contractor, which have significantly eroded during the past two decades. When comparing compensation packages between the two forms of contract, do not be misled by an initial impression that for virtually identical jobs, independent contractors receive better compensation.

There is almost always a price associated with freedom. Do not overlook the costs of (a) full contribution to Social Security tax, (b) health insurance premiums, (c) professional liability coverage, (d) professional organization memberships, (e) publications, seminars, and continuing medical education, (f) accountants and lawyers, (g) employer contribution to retirement plans and costs of establishing and maintaining a private retirement plan, and (h) your time devoted to the obligations of an independent contractor. Unless you are extremely confident in your ability to evaluate alternative compensation packages, consult an accountant. Some independent contractor compensation formulas cannot be adequately evaluated without obtaining historical financial data to verify oral representations. Be cautious about compensation plans predicated in whole or in part on fees collected. Initial income may be significantly delayed and can be prematurely terminated at the end of the contract.

3. Working Schedule: Except as specifically prohibited by the contract, employers have authority to dictate working schedules. In theory, independent contractors have much greater flexibility to accept or reject proposed working schedules. The reality of that flexibility varies considerably from group to group. If flexibility is important to you, you should closely scrutinize that provision of the contract and talk with other physicians in the group to determine how much flexibility actually exists. Some independent contractor agreements do not guarantee a minimum number of hours or shifts. Remember that oral promises are seldom enforceable when there is a written agreement. To the extent possible, if minimums are important to your decision, insist that they be in writing.

4. Rights and Duties: Virtually all contracts contain paragraphs that spell out the rights and duties of each party. It is beyond the scope of this chapter to discuss those rights and duties in detail, but a few words of caution are in order. Some contract provisions contain confusing legal jargon for the specific purpose of complying with state or federal law, JCAHO, or some other regulatory requirements. Such jargon is seldom required in contract provisions that itemize rights and duties (sometimes called *responsibilities* or *obligations*). Provisions that are ambiguous, overly broad, confusing, or inconsistent should be avoided. There are two basic rules for writing such provisions: (a) say what you mean and (b) mean what you say. You and your lawyer should seek written clarification of provisions that do not meet those rules. Although groups and/or hospitals are reluctant to revise

contract provisions for an individual physician, they are often willing to accept clarifying addenda. You should also carefully evaluate the pros and cons of "claims-made" versus "occurrence" policies (this subject is discussed in detail in Chapter 5). Most contracts require physicians to comply with certain laws, government regulations, and JCAHO. Most emergency physicians, during residency, develop a reasonable understanding of their legal duties. If a proposed contract refers to laws, rules, or regulations with which you are not familiar, inquire further. Failure to comply could result in unexpected consequences, including termination and tort liability. Ignorance of your legal duty is not particularly persuasive when the applicable law or regulation is specifically cited in the contract.

5. Termination Provisions: Termination provisions are discussed in greater detail in Chapter 9. Employment agreements usually provide physicians the same degree of security provided to other institutional employees. Independent contractor termination provisions vary tremendously. They often contain no specific term and can be terminated with short notice and with little or no cause. As previously indicated, easy termination provisions may be viewed by the courts and the IRS as suggestive of an employment agreement. It is often difficult or impossible to negotiate termination provisions, but you should at least know what you are getting into. The contract should clearly answer the following questions:
   a. If both parties are happy, will the contract automatically renew? If so, will compensation be reevaluated or altered? Will action be required by you to renew the contract beyond its initial term?
   b. Under what circumstances can the contract be prematurely terminated by the hospital or group? What are the mechanisms for such early termination? Is there a mechanism for notice and an opportunity to correct deficiencies before termination? Are there penalties associated with early termination? How will termination affect medical staff status? Do you have any due process rights of hearing or appeal? What impact will termination have on malpractice insurance?

6. Restrictive Covenants: Most states, to varying degrees, permit restrictive covenants (see Chapter 9 for a more detailed discussion of convenants not to compete). Employment agreements usually tie restrictions to the geographical vicinity of a single hospital or health care system. Independent contractor agreements with groups may be much broader. They may restrict contact with all hospitals to which the group provides

services without identifying them by name. Make sure you know the exact scope of stated restrictions. Basically, enforceability of restrictive covenants is inversely related to their stringency. Restrictions must be rationally related to the legitimate business needs of the imposing party. No clear rules can be articulated because reasonableness varies tremendously depending on geography, local business practices, and the specific relationship between the parties. Because virtually all contractual relationships eventually terminate, do not enter into a contract that contains restrictive covenants you are not ready to live with.

7. Malpractice Insurance and Liability: Employees are generally provided malpractice insurance by their employer. Independent contractors are generally responsible for obtaining and paying for their own insurance. Many groups facilitate acquisition of insurance but do so at some risk because the IRS looks at the procurement of insurance when evaluating employee versus independent contractor status. It is certainly easier to let someone else find and pay for your insurance. You can be reasonably certain that hospitals will provide adequate insurance because hospital assets are at risk if insurance is inadequate. Although most groups are equally conscientious, their motivation is not quite as strong. Physician groups may not be liable for the conduct of physicians with whom they establish an independent contractor relationship. Their potential liability under theories of agency and apparent agency vary from state to state. Even if they are potentially liable, physician groups seldom have significant attachable assets. Because physician groups are almost always corporations, owners may be shielded from personal liability for the conduct of other physicians who work for and through the group. All forms of insurance are typically more expensive if acquired by an individual without group purchasing power. Price, although important, is not always a deciding factor. Above all else, an insurer must have the money and structure to satisfy potential liabilities. Another factor worth consideration is the competence of legal counsel customarily retained by the insurer. Some insurers that do not specialize in professional liability retain legal counsel who lack special competence to handle such cases.

8. Medical Staff Status: Virtually all hospital employment contracts require medical staff membership and adherence to medical staff bylaws, rules, and regulations. There are three issues worthy of consideration:

a. What have you agreed to? Medical staff bylaws or rules and regulations seldom impose significant burdens on emergency physicians. However, because you have agreed to abide by those documents, you should read them to make sure there are no surprises. Unless you are reasonably familiar with the structure of such documents, you may want to have them briefly reviewed by legal counsel with the appropriate expertise.

b. Do the medical staff bylaws provide you with due process before termination? Many physicians and legal commentators suggest that physicians, whether employees, independent contractors, or physicians in private practice, should always retain the right to exercise due process provisions contained in medical staff bylaws. JCAHO requires "due process" protection for all medical staff members before privileges are involuntarily removed. The hospital or contract holder will likely ask you to waive your right to a "due process" hearing if your contract is terminated. From the hospital's point of view, it does not want to lose control of who staffs the emergency department. This has the potential to become a very contentious issue in your negotiating. A reasonable "middle ground" may be to agree that termination of your contract for business/employment issues does not require a "due process" hearing but that termination for quality of care issues could not occur without appropriate "due process."

c. Loss of medical staff membership on termination. Like (b) above, this is a controversial issue among some physicians and attorneys but is seldom of great significance in emergency contracts. The majority of emergency physician contracts provide that medical staff membership and privileges end with contract termination. In the vast majority of cases, the emergency physician has no interest in maintaining medical staff membership if he or she is no longer working as an emergency physician at the institution. This is really a nonissue unless you anticipate specific circumstances by which you would benefit from continued medical staff membership.

9. Billing: Individual emergency physicians are seldom responsible for sending out bills and collecting payment. Such services are usually performed by the hospital for employed physicians. Groups often retain billing and collection services. However, if compensation is based on billings or collections, you cannot completely ignore this unpleasant aspect of your profession. Make certain your contract allows access to necessary financial data. At least occasionally, verify the accuracy of computations by others.

Conclusion

- A perfect contract does not guarantee a successful working relationship. Conversely, one may find a wonderful working relationship despite an atrocious contract.
- Effective negotiation consists of more than achieving the desired contractual language.
- Good interpersonal relationships should not be sacrificed to obtain the perfect contract.
- Considerable caution should be exercised before engaging in vigorous confrontation.
- Do not sour a good deal over relatively insignificant contractual disagreements.

Conversely, unreasonable obstinance or rigidity by a hospital or group may herald an unsatisfactory working relationship.

7

PROMOTION AND TENURE

When seeking a faculty position in an academic institution, there are some additional factors to consider. Most of these additional considerations involve the promotion and tenure process. Although there is great variability in tenure processes among academic institutions and it will be important to understand the specifics for the institution with which you are negotiating, there are some common concepts and principles that can assist you in assessing academic opportunities.

Before proceeding to the discussion of academic promotion, it may be helpful to point out some of the differences in the contracting process in academic institutions. In general, the contracting process in an academic institution is a bit more complicated than that encountered in most community hospitals. Often, there is a standard contract that applies to all faculty members, regardless of discipline. This contract will usually cover general terms of employment, benefits, and grievance and termination procedures. The terms of the general contract are not usually negotiable. In addition to the general contract, it is usually necessary to negotiate terms specific to employment in the home department. These terms should be specified in a letter of agreement signed by the department head. Some appropriate items for inclusion are:

- Clinical and nonclinical hours.
- Specific nonclinical responsibilities, including research, education, and administrative responsibilities.
- Allocations (time and funding) for continuing medical education.
- Specific aspects of your individual schedule, including allocation of night and weekend shifts.

Academic positions will usually entail a greater degree of nonclinical responsibility than do positions in community hospitals. Responsibilities for medical student and resident education, research and publication program and curriculum development, and administrative activities should be spelled out in detail, and you must ensure that adequate time is allocated for attending to these responsibilities.

Most institutions have a number of tracks that new faculty members can follow. Selection of or assignment to a track will depend on the faculty member's career goals and the job description of his or her specific position. Tracks are of two major types: those that lead to tenure and those that do not (nontenure tracks). Among the nontenure tracks, there are usually separate tracks for salaried and nonsalaried faculty. Nonsalaried faculty members are usually those who are salaried by affiliated hospitals. The granting of tenure involves some degree of guaranteed salary support by the university; therefore, it is usually not possible to be on a tenure track unless your salary is at least partially paid by the university. Academic titles for nonsalaried faculty members often are preceded by a clinical modifier (e.g., clinical professor of emergency medicine). For nonsalaried faculty, promotion to associate professor and ultimately full professor is generally based on contribution to the department and hospital, along with regional or national recognition in the specialty (Figure 1, page 61).

Some faculty members salaried by the university will also be in nontenure tracks. These are usually faculty members with primary responsibility for clinical care, clinical supervision of residents, and clinical administration. They generally are not expected to be heavily involved in research or undergraduate (medical student) education, and there usually is no requirement for them to pursue external funding. Although publishing is generally encouraged, there usually is no specific requirement for peer-review publication. Promotion to associate professor and ultimately full professor is largely dependent on clinical, administrative, and educational service and usually requires regional or national recognition in the specialty (Figure 2, page 62).

Faculty members in tenure tracks have very specific and stringent requirements placed on them (Table 1, page 63). The early years, usually five to seven years, are designated as the probationary period. The tenure track faculty member has this time to amass academic credentials sufficient to gain promotion to associate professor. All faculty members are expected to provide service to the home department, hospital, college, university, and specialty. This service requirement is usually met through clinical, administrative, committee, public service, and professional organization work. Building on this foundation, the tenure track faculty member is also required to produce academically. Traditionally, this has meant the publication of original research in peer-review journals and the attainment of external funding, preferably federal funding.

Many institutions have liberalized these requirements, giving greater recognition to teaching contribution, nonfederal funding, and peer-review publications other than original research (e.g., case reports and review articles). Non-peer-review publications, such as book chapters, may be taken into account but generally carry much less weight than peer-review publications. Liberalization of criteria is extremely important for a specialty like emergency medicine, where there usually is a heavy clinical commitment and often there is only the beginnings of a research infrastructure and few mentors for junior faculty to work with.

Liberalization of criteria for promotion is usually accomplished through the establishment of multiple tenure tracks. Some tracks maintain the traditional requirements for peer-review publication and external funding and are appropriate for basic science researchers and full-time researchers in clinical departments. Realistically, few clinicians will have sufficient protected time to achieve success in a traditional research track. There may be no public distinction made between the traditional research track and the "liberalized" clinician's track, both carrying unmodified titles, such as professor of emergency medicine.

Another modification of the tenure and promotion process that is very beneficial to junior faculty is the introductory rank (Figure 2, page 62). This is an initial rank, often entitled instructor, which is not designated as tenure track or nontenure track. This allows the junior faculty member 1 to 2 years in which to acclimatize to the faculty role, get his or her boards completed, and decide on the appropriate career path before beginning the probationary period.

It is difficult to comment on specific requirements for promotion in the various tracks, because there is great institutional variability. For tenure track faculty members in clinical departments, there virtually is always a requirement for peer-review publication, at a sustained rate of at least two or three publications per year during the probationary period. Attainment of significant external funding carries similar weight to publication in the promotion and tenure process and may modify the publication requirement (Table 1, page 63).

Traditionally, the education requirement has been met only through involvement in undergraduate (medical student) education. Liberalization has brought greater credit for graduate medical (resident) education activities, but the importance of undergraduate medical education activities should not be overlooked.

Although switching from one track to another in not usually encouraged, it is usually possible during the early years of the probationary period to move from the tenure track to a non-tenure track. In addition to the usual annual evaluations conducted by the department head, most institutions will have a formal mid-probationary review that is intended to provide mid-term assessment of the faculty member's progress toward promotion.

After completion of a number of years of service to the institution, a faculty member may apply for a sabbatical leave of absence for the purpose of study, research, or other projects designed to increase the faculty member's usefulness to the institution. Sabbaticals are typically for periods of one or two semesters. Although not always specifically limited to tenured faculty members, the granting of sabbaticals to nontenured faculty is rare. While on sabbatical,

FIGURE 1.
TYPICAL PROMOTION AND TENURE
SYSTEM FOR NON-SALARIED FACULTY

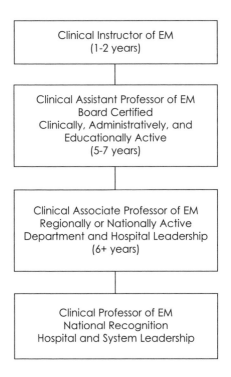

Clinical Instructor of EM
(1-2 years)

Clinical Assistant Professor of EM
Board Certified
Clinically, Administratively, and
Educationally Active
(5-7 years)

Clinical Associate Professor of EM
Regionally or Nationally Active
Department and Hospital Leadership
(6+ years)

Clinical Professor of EM
National Recognition
Hospital and System Leadership

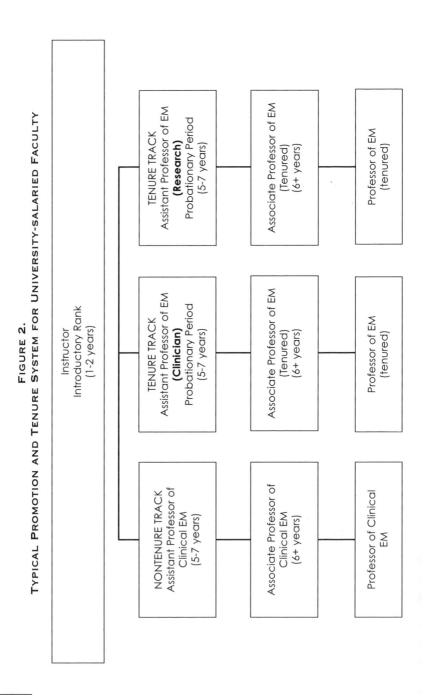

FIGURE 2.
TYPICAL PROMOTION AND TENURE SYSTEM FOR UNIVERSITY-SALARIED FACULTY

TABLE 1.
SAMPLE CRITERIA FOR PROMOTION IN AN ACADEMIC CLINICIAN
TENURE TRACK FOR EMERGENCY MEDICINE FACULTY

CRITERION	AT MIDCYCLE REVIEW	FOR PROMOTION TO ASSOCIATE PROFESSOR	FOR PROMOTION TO PROFESSOR
Patient Care	• Clinical competence • Customer service • Staff relationships • Reliability	• Clinical competence • Customer service • Staff relationships • Reliability	• Clinical competence • Customer service • Staff relationships • Reliability
Administrative Duties	• Clinical liaison function (or equivalent) • Additional assigned area of responsibility	• Clinical liaison function (or equivalent) • Additional assigned area of responsibility	• Clinical liaison function (or equivalent) • Additional assigned area of responsibility
Faculty Development	• 50% Attendance at department sessions • 1 Addition at faculty development activity per year	• 50% Attendance at department sessions • 1 Addition at faculty development activity per year	• 50% Attendance at department sessions • 1 Addition at faculty development activity per year
Stature in Speciality	• 1 Regional committee membership • Regional Presentation	3 points from list below: • 1 Regional committee Member = 1 Chair = 3 • Regional board member or officer = 3 • National committee member = 3 • Regional presentation = 1 • National presentation = 3	6 points from list to left or below: • National or international board member or officer = 6 • International presentation = 3
Committees	• 1 Departmental committee • 2 Hospital, college or university committees	• 2 Departmental committees (or equivalent) • 4 Hospital, college or university committees	• 2 Departmental committees (or equivalent) • 4 Hospital, college or university committees
Teaching	• 1 Year of documented excellence in teaching	• 3 Years of documented excellence in teaching	• 3 Years of documented excellence in teaching
Scholarly Productivity	8 Points*	20 Points*	40 Points*

a faculty member continues to be salaried. For long-term faculty member (e.g., more than 6 years of service), funding may continue at 100% of the regular salary. When faculty members have accrued fewer years of service, salary may be provided at a partial percentage.

When faculty members are funded by multiple sources, such as a university and a practice plan, sabbatical funding may be limited to that portion of the income that comes directly from the university. Portions of salary generated from patient revenues may not be included. Whenever sabbatical leaves of absence are considered, the faculty member must be clear on the specific rules applicable in his or her institution and in his or her specific case.

Climbing the academic ladder is a long, rigorous process. It is, however, the primary way for dedicated academicians to achieve recognition. The achievement of tenure conveys some degree of job security and guaranteed salary support by the university, but its primary function is an acknowledgment of the faculty member's academic achievement and status in the academic community.

Clinical competence is to be determined by the chief of service based on direct observation; chart review; complaint investigation; nursing, resident, and peer feedback; and other pertinent observations as available. Customer service orientation will be determined by the chief of service primarily based on patient and family feedback, complaint investigation, and patient survey results as available. Staff relationships will be determined by feedback from referring and consulting physicians, peers in the department, nursing, and ancillary staffs. Reliability refers to a very high degree of dependability in regard to ensuring coverage of clinical shifts once assigned.

*SCHOLARLY PRODUCTIVITY:

Authorship or editing of textbooks	2.0 points	Letters, reviews, abstracts		0.5
Authorship or editing of monographs	1.0	Authorship of full article non-peer-review publication		0.5
Authorship of peer-reviewed publications		Authorship of book chapters		0.5
Original research, 1st author	2.0	Major federal grant applications ($500,000)		1.0
Original research, 2nd author	1.0	Major federal funding		2.0
Original research, 3rd author	0.5	Minor federal (<$500,000) and non-federal grant applications		0.5
Other full articles, 1st author	1.0	Minor federal and nonfederal funding		1.0
Other full articles, 2nd author	0.5			

8

LEGAL, CONTRACTUAL, AND ADMINISTRATIVE ISSUES RELATED TO MEDICAL BILLING

Despite legal rights and employment agreements, emergency physicians typically have little control over their actual billing and collections. Further, this is perhaps one of the least understood aspects of emergency physician practice. This chapter will help dispel these mysteries and expose some myths related to medical billing and collections. It also summarizes topics related to compensation, reassignment, physician group structure, documentation/coding, and regulatory compliance.

Physicians who provide medical care to patients have a right to collect a fee for services rendered. But emergency medicine practice is somewhat unique in that physicians typically work in a group and do not collect fees from patients on an individual basis. Instead, the hospital or group bills and collects professional fees generated by the physician and provides compensation in accordance with the physician's employment agreement (i.e., contract). By entering into an employment agreement, the physician trades his or her individual right to collect professional fees in exchange for compensation in the form of a salary, an hourly rate, a percent of billings or collections, or any number of other compensation schemes. This practice is called "reassignment" and is typically used regardless of the type of physician group (e.g., democratic, Contract Management Group [CMG], hospital employee, etc.).

BILLING AND FAIR COMPENSATION

Fair compensation is often in the "eye of the beholder" and depends on many factors: locale; academic versus private practice versus CMG; public versus for profit versus nonprofit hospital; patient demographics (i.e., payer mix);

part-time versus full-time; partner versus nonpartner; and many others. Emergency physician compensation surveys are available to help judge the market, but compensation varies considerably even within local regions. Further, a "paycheck" is only part of total compensation. Others, such as retirement plans and benefits such as paid vacations, CME expenses, insurance (health, life, disability, etc.), significantly affect total compensation. Finally, the cost of medical malpractice and "tail" coverage (called "extended reporting period" when leaving the group) needs to be considered as these may not be included in the benefits package.

Physicians have a legal right under Medicare to know what is billed to Medicare under their name. But in most states, there is no similar right to this information for any other payer unless provided for in the physician's employment agreement. Regardless, total billed charges are perhaps the least useful measure to use when considering fair compensation. What is actually collected ranges from 20% to 80% of billed charges but is typically about 35% after bad debt, contractual reductions, and Medicare/Medicaid payments are taken into account. Billing/collections expenses range from 5% to 20% of collections, but typically cost 5% to 10%. Benefits will account for roughly 20% to 25%, and malpractice, 10% to 20%. Other overhead includes administrative expenses, which are typically 2% to 5% of collections.

When all is said and done, the typical emergency physician will take home roughly 15% to 20% of billed charges. This may be a shock to some and has been the source of considerable misunderstanding for those who fail to understand America's rather perverse system of medical billing, especially in emergency care. Because of this, the real opportunity toward better physician compensation lies more in effective charting, billing, coding, collections, payer contract negotiations, and benefits management (i.e., cost of malpractice and other insurance, retirement, etc.) than in any other factor.

Large multihospital physician groups (CMG's, corporate democratic groups, etc.) are often more adept at creating economies of scale and reducing overhead expenses. Single hospital or small democratic physician groups offer more opportunities for partnership and autonomy but may not have as much ability to control certain administrative expenses. In recent years, the advantages of small emergency physician group practices are increasingly outweighed by the efficiencies available to large corporate emergency physician groups with regard to total compensation. Billing and malpractice insurance costs are the primary factors in this transition.

MEDICAL BILLING AND PAYER CONTRACTS

In addition to the employment agreement, physicians must sign a variety of other contracts, including government (e.g., Medicare, Medicaid, Champus, etc.) and perhaps even contracts with individual private payers. These are fairly standard and there is little room for negotiation. Nevertheless, these contracts personally obligate the signer for the details outlined in the agreement.

The Medicare contract is particularly onerous, and state Medicaid contracts can be as well. Physicians are personally liable for Medicare fraud even though they have assigned their right to bill Medicare to their employer and even though they may have had nothing to do with the commission of the fraud. Other examples include EMTALA, where significant responsibilities are assumed by the physician by virtue of their agreement with the hospital to provide emergency department services rather than due to their Medicare contract.

Compliance with these contracts is relatively straightforward, but one should be assured that the physician group (including its billing company or process) and hospital have reasonable and sufficient compliance procedures in place. Further, be wary of schemes that may create increased personal risk.

For example, certain hospitals have initiated "deferral of care" programs where, in an effort to redirect "nonurgent" patients from the emergency department, patients are required to pay up front or seek care elsewhere. Emergency physicians may be required to participate in such programs and must assess their EMTALA and other Medicare/Medicaid liability risk. Asking the hospital to cover liability (EMTALA, malpractice, etc.) under these circumstances is entirely reasonable.

Also be wary of ill-conceived billing enhancement schemes. For example, some groups require physicians to "buff up their charts" after the fact, if the coding reveals missing data elements that would allow a higher charge. This can place the physician in a precarious position if they subsequently document things they may not have actually done. The opportunity to document right is the first time. Subsequent feedback on how it can be done better the next time is entirely appropriate, but altering the chart after the fact may create undue risk.

REASSIGNMENT OF PHYSICIAN PAYMENT

Medicare and other payers generally make payments directly to the beneficiary (patient) unless there is an "assignment of benefits" to the physician or entity that performed the services. Certain payers do not allow reassignment for noncontracted physicians, forcing collection directly from the patient. But most insurance payments are sent directly to the billing company "lock box" in the name of the group and often for bulk amounts regardless of the physician providing the service. Be careful to always check office/hospital mail. Physicians occasionally receive checks in the mail addressed personally to them and are usually required by contract to turn these over to the group.

For physicians to receive Medicare payments directly, they must "accept Medicare assignment." This also means they agree to accept Medicare's reimbursement as payment in full excluding deductibles and co-payments that must be collected from the patient. Regardless, Medicare-contracted physicians may not bill patients for the difference between billed charges and Medicare approved payment (i.e., balance bill). If the physician does not "accept assignment," they may bill slightly more but are still regulated by the Medicare fee schedule and must collect the entire payment from the patient. Virtually all physicians "accept assignment" from Medicare and may be required to do so by the physician group. Note that the Medicare contract and "assignment" cover all patients for whom a physician bills Medicare regardless of the hospital or group.

In the past, IRS rulings and Medicare's strict rules (an attempt to prevent fraud and abuse) governing the ability of physicians to assign Medicare program rights to other entities forced most groups to require emergency physicians to become employees rather than independent contractors. While most of these rules have now changed, there are (mostly tax) advantages and disadvantages to being an independent contractor versus an employee. Nevertheless, the vast majority of emergency physicians are employees, even if they are also owners/partners.

CODING COMPLIANCE

As previously noted, proper documentation and coding have significant potential to improve compensation. It is very important for physicians to know and document the required elements necessary for appropriate coding. Coders can only code what is documented, even if it might otherwise seem obvious. This will directly affect the revenue of group and indirectly individual physician compensation.

Who performs the coding varies, but most groups use professional coders in-house or outsourced as part of the billing process. As noted, physicians are personally responsible for the accuracy of the coding and billing, so be assured that the process being used has an acceptable compliance program. Due to the complexity of emergency medicine coding, it is generally inadvisable for emergency physicians to do their own coding.

"Issues such as accountability for coding, billing processes, education, monitoring, and discipline, must be incorporated in any formalized compliance program developed by the group, hospital, or individual emergency physicians. Contractual relationships between emergency physicians and their employers and/or practice locations need to clearly delineate compliance responsibilities. It is evident that development and implementation of an effective and usable compliance program is rapidly becoming an industry standard. Compliance programs are a powerful tool to promote a strong ethical approach to coding/billing and might provide at least a partial mitigation of any penalties resulting from a government audit or fraud investigation."[1]

For more information on fraud and compliance related to medical billing, consult "Fraud, Compliance, & Emergency Medicine."[1]

BILLING FRAUD AND ABUSE

The Centers for Medicare & Medicaid Service (CMS) along with other government agencies have jurisdiction over the Medicare and Medicaid programs. As such, they actively monitor and investigate fraud and abuse for inappropriate billing. For emergency medicine, such cases typically involve accusations of "upcoding" (coding higher than the documentation supports).

True fraud should be differentiated from mere billing errors. In fact, CMS allows up to 5% errors as a safe harbor, but beyond that they may pursue abuse or fraud charges. A billing "error" may require repayment with interest. "Abuse" (activities inconsistent with accepted practices) may result in repayment plus monetary penalties. "Fraud" (intentional deception) includes all the above, plus possible exclusion from Medicare and could result in criminal prosecution leading incarceration.

CMS routinely does random, prospective, and investigative audits. Compliance is relatively easy, but it is obviously very important. All commercial billing companies have coding compliance procedures in place, although despite this some have been prosecuted for fraud and abuse. Although the individual physician is ultimately responsible for what is billed on their behalf, coding issues found on behalf of an independent coding company rarely result in the physician being held criminally responsible.

The real risk for physicians is through intentional or inadvertent fraud by documenting elements that were not done. Such behavior is often facilitated by the use of paper templates or electronic charting where "over"-documentation can occur with simple check marks or computerized autopopulation of charting elements. Another potentially dangerous practice is the use of the "Review of Systems" (ROS) comment, "All other systems reviewed and are normal." This requires that all 14 systems be assessed, a difficult feat. Because only 10 systems are required to achieve the maximum for this billing element, one should weigh carefully how the ROS element is documented.

Although most cases of fraud are found by audits, a Qui Tam ("whistleblower") suit can be an insidious source leading to an investigation. The whistleblower (often a disgruntled former employee) stands to benefit financially (15% to 25% of the judgment), so be aware that others may be watching.

DOCUMENTATION

Documentation to support the maximal allowable code is beyond the scope of this chapter, but it is imperative to know what documentation and coding responsibilities are required. It is also important to receive routine feedback on documentation compliance. These feedback summaries should include for each patient the expected coded level of service and the documented level of service with a notation of missing documentation elements. Also expect monthly and yearly billing summaries that include the total number of patients treated, gross charges, average charge, and a comparison with colleagues. Whether other billing information (i.e., collections) is made available will typically depend upon the employment agreement or position within the group (i.e., partner). Most physician groups (and virtually all other businesses) do not share such financial information with nonpartners/owners.

Until accustomed to the rigors of coding compliant documentation, physicians may wish to use a reminder card or a template to help remember the required elements. General education on this topic is available from a variety of sources and should be done on a regular basis.

EMERGENCY MEDICAL TREATMENT AND LABOR ACT (EMTALA)

Billing issues often occur in the context of EMTALA. Obtaining demographic and billing information, including collection of copayments, is allowable at any point in the emergency department process as long as it does not delay the medical screening examination (MSE) and is not done in an economically coercive way. However, seeking authorization for treatment is expressly prohibited until the MSE is completed and stabilizing treatment initiated. EMTALA is all about nondiscriminatory treatment irrespective of the ability to pay. There are no exceptions for managed care patients or illegal aliens. Nevertheless, in the course of an emergency department visit, billing questions often arise. "Will this be covered by my insurance?" "How much is this going to cost?" Often the safest and perhaps most accurate answer by the physician is simply, "I do not know." It is prudent to allow others to address billing and payment issues and for the physician to focus on treating the patient.

In general, EMTALA compliance is easily achieved by simply taking care of the patient irrespective of their ability to pay or type of insurance. Any time someone is treated differently because of his or her insurance (or lack thereof), the "EMTALA flag" should go up.

WORKING WITH RESIDENTS AND STUDENTS

"The teaching physician must be personally involved in the part (or parts) of service that they determine are the critical or key portions, and must document in the medical record his or her participation in the service. Documentation of key elements in each of these components may be satisfied by a combination of medical record entries made by the resident and the teaching physician. For purposes of payment, E/M services billed by teaching physicians require that they personally document at least the following:

a. That they performed the service or were physically present during the key or critical portions of the service when performed by the resident; and
b. The participation of the teaching physician in the management of the patient.

For the purposes of this discussion, "physically present" means the teaching physician is at the patient's bedside with the resident as opposed to present somewhere in the emergency department."[i]

"The physician cannot use documentation by medical students as part of his/her documentation, except for the Review of Systems (ROS) and Past/Family/Social History (PFSH) for which CMS does not require personal documentation. When ancillary personnel record history elements, the physician must verify and re-document the history of present illness as well as perform and re-document the physical exam and medical decision making activities of the service [if not physically present during collection]. A physician's mere countersigning of the chart does not make the services reimbursable to the physician."[1]

Services performed independently by students are not billable but may be billed if done under the personal supervision of the teaching physician who is performing the service. Services provided by nurse practitioners (NPs) and physician assistants (PAs) with a contractual relationship with the physician group are billable under either the NP/PA provider number (lesser reimbursement), or the supervising physician (full reimbursement) if there is a face-to-face physician encounter with the patient.

BILLING FOR ELECTROCARDIOGRAM AND RADIOLOGY INTERPRETATIONS

Emergency physicians are allowed to bill for these services if done contemporaneous with the emergency department visit and documented appropriately. Because such billing will prevent subsequent payment to the radiologist or cardiologist reading on a delayed basis, this is often a political issue that must be decided between all parties. But regardless it is important to know how to document such interpretations.

PROFESSIONAL COURTESY

Professional courtesy is allowable with certain restrictions but will vary hospital by hospital. Also, billing for "insurance only" (i.e., waiving copayments and deductibles) can be problematic. Be sure to know what the group/hospital's policy is in this regard and be careful about making promises when it may be unclear if the patient will actually receive this courtesy. Remember, the patient will also receive a facility (hospital) billed charge, which the physician may not be authorized to waive.

SUMMARY

Medical billing is the lifeblood of emergency medicine and must be done well, often under the worst of all circumstances. Active involvement in this process by all physicians is the key to being successful and staying out of trouble. Increasing financial pressure, in large part due unfunded mandates and the uninsured, tends to create ill-conceived schemes to limit financial risk in the emergency department. It is incumbent upon the prudent emergency physician to be informed and always vigilant in what amounts to the most regulated industry in the world.

When it comes to payment, physicians are not paid for good medical care. They are paid for documentation of the care they provided. Up to a point, the better that documentation, the better is the compensation.

Finally, being a physician is more than about money. Treating patients fairly in all respects, including the billing process, should be an overriding objective.

REFERENCES

1. American College of Emergency Physicians (August 2004). *Fraud, Compliance, & Emergency Medicine*. Dallas, TX, ACEP. Available at http://www.acep.org/webportal/PracticeResources/issues/reimb/compliance/.

9

TERMINATION OF CONTRACT

Editor's Note: Most contracts are entered into by both parties with optimism. However, the physician must remember the essence of contracts is the allocation of anticipated risk. Even the most collegial relationships bear the risk of future disenchantment or simply changed circumstances. This chapter discusses the means by which a contract is terminated. The legalities of the controversial "noncompete" clauses are discussed in depth.

When entering into a business or professional relationship, it is human nature to focus on the opportunities that hopefully lie ahead rather than on the unpleasant consequences if the arrangement does not work out. As a consequence, physicians, like others, often may pay too little attention to the termination provision of their contracts.

Before executing an employment or independent contractor agreement, and especially when contemplating the termination of an existing contract, it is crucial to understand the term of the contract, the ways in which the contract can be terminated before the end of the term, the consequences of termination, and the rights and obligations that will continue after termination. A physician who fails to understand and negotiate these provisions may be surprised to discover that he or she does not have the desired job security or freedom to pursue other opportunities or that he or she faces other adverse consequences on termination.

This chapter discusses some of the principal issues to consider when negotiating the termination provisions of a contract and when contemplating the consequences of termination.

Although emergency physicians enter into employment and independent contractor agreements with group practices, hospitals, physician staffing organizations, and other entities, for simplicity this chapter refers to the employer or other entity retaining the physician as the "practice." The employment or independent contractor agreement is referred to in this chapter as the "contract."

TERM AND GROUNDS FOR TERMINATION

Absent unusual circumstances, an employee who does not have a written employment agreement will be deemed to be an "employee at will."

In general, either the employer or the employee is free to terminate an employment at will relationship without prior notice, so long as the termination is not in violation of legal prohibitions on discrimination and related public policy concerns.

When a written contract exists, an employment or independent contractor relationship will continue during the term of the contract, subject to termination on the grounds set forth in the contract or by operation of law. A contract can terminate in a number of ways, the most common of which are (1) expiration of the term set forth in the contract, (2) termination by agreement between the practice and physician, (3) termination by one of the parties without cause, (4) termination by one of the parties for cause, or (5) automatic termination on the occurrence of an event specified in the contract. Some contracts have a specific term, such as 1 or more years. Other contracts have open-ended terms that will continue unless and until terminated as provided in the contract.

A careful review of the term and termination provision in a contract will sometimes reveal that a contract with a fixed term contains an "evergreen clause" that automatically continues the contract or that the contract is subject to early termination. An evergreen clause provides that the contract will be automatically renewed for successive additional terms until either party provides written notice of termination or nonrenewal.

Contracts often allow either party or both parties to terminate the contract without cause. For example, either party may be allowed to terminate on 30 days' written notice, in which case a physician who signed an apparent long-term contract with the expectation of receiving job security may be dismayed to discover that he or she is only assured of employment for 1 month. A physician who desires job security should negotiate for either the deletion of the practice's right to terminate without cause or a lengthy notice period.

Contracts typically allow the practice (and, in some cases, the physician) to terminate the contract "for cause" on grounds specified in the contract. Some contracts contain broad, subjective standards that threaten the physician's job security by allowing the practice to terminate the contract if the practice determines that the physician's conduct is not in the best interests of the practice.

The grounds to terminate the contract should be analyzed carefully to ensure that the "for cause" termination standards are objective and reasonable. To the extent possible, subjective matters should be removed as grounds for termination or the provisions should be modified into objective, verifiable standards. For example, a provision allowing termination for "moral turpitude" or "conduct that diminishes the reputation of the practice" should be deleted or should be replaced by a provision setting forth specific, objective standards, such as conviction of a felony arising out of violation of the state's medical practice act. Moreover, a provision allowing the practice to terminate for any "material breach" of the contract should require the practice to provide the physician with written notice and a reasonable opportunity to correct (or "cure") the breach within a specified period of time, such as 30 days.

It is not uncommon for a contract to set forth one-sided termination provisions that allow the practice to terminate the contract but do not include a corresponding right for the physician to terminate the contract. After all, most contracts are drafted by the attorneys for the practice. The physician should negotiate parallel termination rights. In particular, if the practice is allowed to terminate without cause, the employee should be entitled to terminate on the same terms. Moreover, the employee should negotiate for the right to terminate for cause on any breach by the practice or on the practice's failure to operate in compliance with legal or ethical requirements. Please keep in mind that an otherwise innocent and diligent physician can be tainted by the practice's violation of law and may even face sanctions (e.g., exclusion from Medicare and fines) based on the conduct of the practice with respect to the physician's patients. The physician may also consider negotiating for a right to terminate if the practice loses or amends a particular contract (e.g., a hospital emergency services agreement) or assigns the contract with the physician, or on the sale or merger of the practice.

Automatic termination occurs on specified events, such as the death of a physician and sometimes the physician's permanent disability. Additional automatic termination events may be added, such as the loss of an emergency services agreement or the dissolution of the practice.

When terminating a contract, it is important to comply with all termination requirements as set forth in the contract. In particular, all technicalities for notice should be followed. For example, if termination section requires written notice and the notice section requires that all notices be sent by certified or registered mail, return receipt requested, the notice should comply with this requirement to remove any doubt that the notice is effective.

If a physician terminates a contract before the time allowed under the contract, he or she will be in breach of the contract and therefore may be liable to the practice for any damages incurred by the practice as a result of the premature termination and may be precluded from asserting claims against the practice. In addition, the terminating physician may be subject to some of the consequences discussed in the next section of this chapter.

CONSEQUENCES OF TERMINATION

A physician should consider the consequences of termination when negotiating the contract and when determining whether to terminate the contract or respond to termination by the practice.

Depending on the terms of the contract, a practice or physician may find it advantageous to terminate a contract for cause, rather than without cause. A contract can typically be terminated immediately if the requirements of the "for cause" termination section are satisfied, whereas termination without cause typically requires prior notice unless employment is at will.

Furthermore, the rights and obligations of the physician and the practice are sometimes affected by the method of termination. For example, the provisions of a contract may require a physician who is terminated for cause to pay for "tail" coverage or forfeit severance pay or deferred compensation. The physician should review the contract and all pension, profit-sharing, severance, deferred compensation, and similar employee benefit plans to determine the impact of termination on his or her benefits. Such plans often contain vesting schedules that would require the physician to forfeit benefits if his or her employment terminates before achieving a specified level of seniority.

The physician should confirm that he or she has received all compensation and other benefits to which he or she is entitled. In many states, an employee (but not an independent contractor) is entitled to compensation for accrued but unused vacation time. Contracts sometimes entitle a physician to severance pay or to compensation based on collections for his or her accounts receivable. A physician who is not diligently guarding his or her rights may be shortchanged, whether intentionally or inadvertently.

A practice is generally free to terminate a physician for any reason or for no reason, except as otherwise provided in his or her contract or as prohibited by law. An employee who believes that he or she has been terminated or had other adverse consequences in violation of his or her contract or applicable law may wish to confer with a qualified attorney to determine his or her rights. For example, federal, state, and local laws prohibit discrimination on various grounds, such as race, religion, national origin, and gender, and place restriction on the ability of employers to take adverse actions against whistle-blowers.

The contract typically entitles the practice or hospital to own patient records and various other documents pertaining to the practice. Therefore, the physician will generally be required to return all records, including photocopies. Access to records and documents could be crucial in responding to a variety of matters, such as malpractice claims, disciplinary investigations, medical staff proceedings, and inquiries from malpractice carriers and payers. In addition, financial records may be necessary to prepare income tax returns or to respond to audits. Therefore, the physician should negotiate for access to records for the purpose of developing a defense or preparing income tax returns.

A practice may present a departing physician with one or more documents to sign. The physician should take care not to sign any documents that he or she does not understand, particularly if the documents refer to the release, settlement, or waiver of any rights or claims. By signing, the employee may inadvertently give up rights and release the practice from its obligations.

Before signing any release or settlement documents, a physician should obtain the advice of an attorney to evaluate the consequences of the documents and protect his or her interests.

Continuing Obligations

Most contract obligations end with the contract, allowing a physician to escape unsatisfactory conditions by resigning. Some obligations, however, may continue for years after termination. "Tail" coverage and noncompetition obligations warrant particular attention, because they can be expensive in terms of both out-of-pocket costs and lost opportunities.

"Tail" Coverage Responsibilities

As discussed in Chapter 5, if malpractice insurance is maintained on a claims-made (rather than occurrence) basis, coverage typically ceases when the physician leaves the practice. To provide continuing coverage, the physician would need to obtain a "tail" endorsement or a malpractice policy that provides prior acts coverage.

"Tail" coverage obligations can have a lasting affect. A physician who faces the burden of paying for his or her "tail" coverage may find it necessary to take a position with an employer who provides coverage with a retroactive date covering the physician's services for the prior practice, rather than a position that may provide greater satisfaction or better career opportunities. Moreover, the physician's compensation from subsequent employers may be related to his or her profitability and costs, in which case the higher premiums resulting from the retroactive date may decrease his or her compensation.

Contracts should address the responsibility to obtain "tail" coverage. Due to the expense of "tail" coverage, practices sometimes shift this burden to the physician. The physician should negotiate a requirement that the practice provide "tail" coverage. If the practice refuses to bear this responsibility, then the physician should consider several compromise approaches. Under one alternative, the obligation to pay the "tail" coverage premium could be prorated between the practice and the physician based on the number of years of employment. For example, the practice could be obligated to pay 25% of the premium for each year of employment.

A second approach is to negotiate the "tail" coverage responsibility based on the reason for termination. For example, the practice could bear the premium if the practice terminates the contract without cause, the physician terminates for cause, or the contract terminates due to the death or disability of the physician, and the physician could bear the premium if the physician terminates without cause or the practice terminates for cause.

COVENANTS NOT TO COMPETE

To protect its relationships and proprietary information, a practice will often impose restrictions on a variety of activities, such as negotiating with the hospital, working in the hospital emergency department, hiring personnel, and using or disclosing confidential information. Many contracts even require the physician to resign from the medical staff of the hospital and to waive his or her rights to a fair hearing.

Such restrictions are sometimes referred to as "covenants not to compete," "restrictive covenants," and "noncompetition," "confidentiality," or "nondisclosure" obligations. For the purposes of this chapter, these restrictions are referred to as "covenants not to compete."

A physician who signs a contract without understanding the implications of a covenant not to compete may later discover that he or she is precluded from taking advantage of significant career opportunities. A physician who accepts a subsequent position or starts his or her own practice may be faced with an injunction or substantial financial liability based on a covenant not to compete.

HOSPITAL RELATIONSHIPS

Practices are understandably protective of their contracts and other arrangements to provide services at hospital emergency departments, urgent aid centers, occupational health facilities, and other facilities, particularly in light of the exclusive nature of many of these arrangements. By virtue of relationships he or she establishes as a result of his or her association with the practice, a physician may be in a position to set up a competing practice and to take away a hospital contract from the practice.

Alternatively, a hospital may pursue a divide-and-conquer strategy of terminating its exclusive provider contract with a practice and negotiating a replacement agreement with some of the practice's physicians.

As a means of protecting a practice's relationships with hospitals and other facilities, contracts typically prohibit a physician from negotiating with or providing services for the facilities served by the practice. These restrictions often apply during the term of the contract and for a period of time afterward, such as 1 year.

The physician should pay particular attention to the description of prohibited facilities. Due to mergers, acquisitions, and other affiliations among hospitals, as well as the possibility that a practice may enter into future contracts with additional hospitals and facilities, a covenant that at first glance appears to be limited to a particular hospital may be interpreted to prohibit the physician from working at a number of locations.

Definitions of key terms can result in deceptively broad restrictions, because a term that in common use has a narrow meaning may take on a more expansive meaning. For example, although it may appear obvious that a reference to the "hospital" or a "facility" means the emergency department where a physician provides services, a definition of "hospital" as all facilities owned or operated by a particular hospital or its affiliates would apply not only to the hospital where a physician is assigned but also to ambulatory surgery or urgent aid centers, occupational medicine programs, and other hospitals within the hospital system. Similarly, if a contract defines the term "hospital" as any hospital or other facility where the practice provides medical services, the term would apply to other hospitals and facilities that contract with the practice, whether before or after the signing of the contract.

Contracts sometimes stretch the definition of "hospital" even further by including hospitals and other facilities with which the practice has discussions or negotiations.

The definition of the types of services prohibited by the covenant not to compete should be reviewed to ensure that it is limited to the types of services that compete with the services the physician provides for the practice. A broad definition of "services" in a covenant not to compete may prohibit a physician not only from providing emergency services but also from providing any medical services at the specified facilities.

As a condition for entering into an emergency service agreement with a practice, hospitals often require that the practice obtain the agreement of its physicians to resign from the medical staff and to waive their fair hearing rights on the termination of employment or the practice's loss of its emergency services agreement. The physician may therefore find that he or she will be unable to practice at the hospital after termination.

In some cases, the loss of medical staff privileges could trigger adverse reports to the National Practitioner Data Bank or the state medical board, thereby making it difficult to obtain medical staff privileges at another hospital or a position with another practice. The adverse report could even result in a disciplinary investigation by the state medical board. As a consequence, a physician should request that his or her right to a fair hearing will not be waived if the surrender of medical staff privileges would be reported to the National Practitioner Data Bank or the medical board.

GEOGRAPHICAL RESTRICTIONS

Contracts sometimes prohibit a physician from providing competing services within the practice's geographical area. For example, the physician may be prohibited from providing competing services within a 10-mile radius of certain practice locations. Although this type of restriction is less common in emergency medicine contracts, it is particularly burdensome for the physician because it would require the physician to leave the area even if he or she will not pose a threat to the practice's relationships.

As in the case of hospital restrictions, the definition of services will be important. For example, a restriction that is limited to emergency medicine may be less objectionable than a restriction that applies to all medical services, depending on the individual physician's training and interests. Moreover, geographical restrictions are sometimes more expansive than they appear at first glance. For example, a 10-mile restriction from each practice hospital could encompass a large area if the practice has contracts at three hospitals.

To understand the coverage, the physician should measure the restrictions on a map and draw a circle around each restricted area.

RECRUITMENT OF PRACTICE PERSONNEL

As a means of discouraging the loss of key personnel, the formation of competing groups, and the use of a divide-and-conquer strategy by hospitals, contracts often prohibit the recruitment of practice physicians and other personnel. A physician who is departing from a practice should take care so that his or her comments to practice personnel will not be construed as recruitment or encouragement in violation of a covenant not to compete.

CONFIDENTIALITY

Confidential information often constitutes the most valuable property of a business. A practice, for example, may possess confidential information regarding potential sources of contracts, referral sources, or negotiating strategies. In addition, the practice, as well as the physician, has the obligation to maintain the confidentiality of patient records. The contracts or policy manuals of most practices therefore require the physician to maintain the confidentiality of the practice's confidential information.

Even in the absence of confidentiality provisions and policies, the laws of most states impose an obligation to maintain the confidentiality of trade secrets and may prohibit physicians from using the trade secrets of a practice to the disadvantage of the practice. Although trade secret protections vary by state, a trade secret is sometimes defined as information that is sufficiently secret to derive economic value, actual or potential, from not being generally known to other persons who can obtain economic value from its disclosure or use and is the subject of reasonable efforts to maintain its secrecy or confidentiality.

To determine the scope of his or her confidentiality obligations, a departing physician should review the confidentiality provisions in his or her contract and in any policies developed by the practice. State laws may allow the use and disclosure of information that is publicly available, even if a contract prohibits disclosure.

PENALTIES FOR BREACH OF COVENANT NOT TO COMPETE

A physician who violates a covenant not to compete may be subject to various penalties, based on the terms of the contract. Some of the consequences are discussed below.

Covenants not to compete typically allow the practice to obtain an injunction to prevent the violation of the restrictions. If the court determines that the covenant not to compete is enforceable and that the physician is in breach of the covenant, the court may order injunctive relief prohibiting the physician, and possibly a subsequent employer, from engaging in the prohibited conduct.

Contracts sometimes set forth damages or other financial penalties for the violation of a covenant not to compete. For example, a physician who breaches the covenant not to compete may be required to pay specified damages or to forfeit benefits, such as deferred compensation or severance pay. In other cases, A physician who breaches a covenant not to compete may be required to pay damages to compensate the practice for its losses resulting from the breach or to pay all profits from the physician's breach. In addition, some contracts require the losing party to pay the prevailing party's attorney's fees, which can be substantial. An employer may even have the right to withhold compensation, on the theory that an unfaithful employee forfeits his or her compensation.

ENFORCEMENT OF COVENANTS NOT TO COMPETE

If a practice takes action to enforce a covenant not to compete, the outcome is often crucial for both the practice and the physician. A practice that is unable to enforce a covenant not to compete may face the erosion of its relationships and vitality, whereas a practice that prevails in enforcing a covenant not to compete may be in a position to protect its relationships and prevent competition. Conversely, enforcement of a covenant not to compete may place serious restrictions on the ability of a physician to practice his or her specialty and to earn a livelihood.

Physicians confront various myths about covenants not to compete. For example, on hearing about physicians who have defeated attempts to enforce covenants not to compete, a physician may conclude that such restrictions are illegal and, therefore, unenforceable. On the other hand, a physician or practice may assume that because he or she signed a contract containing a covenant not to compete, he or she will be prohibited from violating the covenant not to compete.

Despite headlines and anecdotes that may suggest otherwise, the ability of a practice to enforce a covenant not to compete is seldom subject to standards that are clear and simple. When determining whether to enforce a covenant not to compete, a judge will base his or her decision on state law as well as the contract provisions at issue and the specific facts of the case. As a consequence, courts confronted with cases that may appear to involve similar contract terms and circumstances may reach opposite conclusions based on nuances in contract terms, the circumstances of particular cases, or applicable state law. For example, without a thorough understanding of state law and the particular circumstances, it may be misleading to rely on a judge's determination in a case involving a specialty that is dependent on relationships with referral sources and patients, rather than with particular hospitals.

Most covenant not to compete issues are governed by state law. The states impose various principles for the interpretation and enforcement of covenants not to compete. For example, some states (including Alabama, Colorado, Delaware, and North Dakota) impose severe limitations on the enforcement of covenants not to compete. Other states are more likely to enforce covenant not to compete obligations. Therefore, the state law governing the interpretation of a contract will have a large impact on the enforceability of a covenant not to compete.

Contracts nearly always specify the governing law. Contractual choice of law provisions are generally accepted by courts unless the court finds compelling public policy reasons to apply the law of a different state. Although standards vary by state, many states focus on whether the restrictions are reasonable in duration, geographical coverage, and scope of activity. To satisfy these standards, the covenant not to compete must not impose unreasonable restrictions on the physician's ability to practice his or her specialty and must be necessary for the protection of the practice's legitimate interests, such as its confidential information and relationships with hospitals, personnel, and, depending on the nature of the practice, patients and referral sources. In addition, the covenant not to compete must not be contrary to the public policy of the state, as set forth in statutes, regulations, and court decisions.

With regard to duration, a covenant not to compete will generally be allowed to continue only so long as the physician is in a position to harm the practice by using confidential information or taking advantage of relationships developed through his or her affiliation with the practice. State law determines whether a court that holds that a covenant not to compete is unreasonably restrictive (and therefore unenforceable as written) has the authority to modify the contract or whether the covenant not to compete is void due to the offending provision. When confronting an overly restrictive provision, courts in some states will reform (or "blue pencil") the offending provisions by modifying the contract to enforce reasonable covenants not to compete that are less restrictive than the offending provisions. In states that are more protective of employees, a covenant not to compete that contains an overly restrictive provision will be void, even with respect to provisions that are reasonable and would be enforced in the absence of the offending provisions. Under the laws of other states, overly restrictive provisions are void, but separate, reasonable provisions in the covenant not to compete are enforceable if the provisions are divisible from the offending provisions.

An understanding of state law regarding reformation of a covenant not to compete is a critical element of negotiating a covenant not to compete and determining the risk arising out of a breach of the covenant not to compete. For example, assume that a contract prohibits a physician from providing medical services at any hospital within a given county and that a physician desires to enter into an exclusive agreement to succeed his or her current practice as the provider of emergency physician services at a particular hospital. Assume further that the countywide restriction is overly broad but that it is reasonable for the practice to prohibit the physician from contracting with the hospital. If state law allows the reformation of offending provisions, the physician would face the risk of an injunction. If, however, the state does not allow the reformation of covenants not to compete, the physician would have a defense to the enforcement of the covenant not to compete.

If a practice sues a physician to enforce a covenant not to compete, various defenses may be available, depending on the circumstances and applicable state law. As discussed earlier, the law of each state imposes restrictions on the enforcement of covenants not to compete, particularly if the restrictions are more expansive than necessary or impose unreasonable restrictions on the physician. A few other possible defenses are discussed here.

In some cases, a court may determine that a practice does not have the right to enforce a contract, even if the restriction is otherwise appropriate. For example, in some states, a hospital or other entity owned and operated by nonphysicians may be precluded from enforcing a covenant not to compete. Moreover, if the practice attempting to enforce a covenant not to compete is not a signatory to the contract, a physician may be able to assert the defense that he or she does not have a contract with the practice and, therefore, is not the subject to the covenant not to compete.

If a physician enters into a covenant not to compete agreement after commencing employment, state law should be examined to determine whether the timing may be asserted as a defense. Under the law of some states, a covenant not to compete that is entered into after the commencement of employment will be void for lack of consideration unless the physician receives an additional benefit, such as a signing bonus. In other states, continued employment will constitute sufficient consideration so long as the continued employment continues for a significant period of time.

A practice that is in material breach of the contract may in some cases be precluded from enforcing the covenant not to compete. The physician, however, should beware of contract provisions that state that a covenant not to compete is "independent" of the other obligations of the parties and that a breach by the practice will not excuse a breach of covenant not to compete.

In light of the uncertainty surrounding covenants not to compete and the stakes for both the practice and the physician, it is crucial to obtain the advice of an attorney who is qualified to analyze the implications of a covenant not to compete.

CONCLUSION

As discussed in this chapter, the termination of a contract can have serious consequences. A physician should, therefore, take care to understand and negotiate termination and covenant not to compete provisions before signing the contract. In addition, before terminating an existing contract, a physician should determine the consequences or termination, particularly if he or she will compete with the practice.